Profession
Without
Community

Studies in Occupations and Professions

Advisor: MARVIN BRESSLER
Princeton University

A Random House Study in Sociology

Robert Perrucci PURDUE UNIVERSITY

Joel E. Gerstl TEMPLE UNIVERSITY

PROFESSION WITHOUT COMMUNITY: ENGINEERS IN AMERICAN SOCIETY

RANDOM HOUSE *New York*

2/1972
Sci.

Acknowledgments

The data reported in this book were drawn from a national survey of engineering graduates in industry and government conducted by Robert Perrucci and William K. LeBold. (The details of the survey are reported in "The Engineer in Industry and Government," *Journal of Engineering Education,* March 1966, pp. 237–273.) Robert Perrucci would also like to thank the National Science Foundation for support of a project entitled "Organizations, Careers, and Professional Performance" (GS1168), which made possible the data analysis presented in this book.

We also acknowledge with appreciation the work of: Ernest J. Cioffi for abstracting relevant research literature, Vincent J. Salvo for assistance in data analysis, and Dena Targ for preparation of the final manuscript.

We dedicate this book to Carolyn and Judy and to San San Bay.

Contents

Profession
Without
Community

1

ENGINEERING AND THE PROFESSIONS IN MODERN SOCIETY

One of the many features that distinguishes modern industrial societies from their historic pasts, as well as from contemporary nonindustrial societies, is a complex and elaborate division of labor. The dissection of a total task into the component activities that will result in an end product has led to increasing specialization of skills in the labor force. Older occupations, which have been largely based upon more informal procedures of transmitting the occupational skill to apprentices, have given way to training programs, licensing systems, and professional schools. Newer occupations have emerged as soon as advances in knowledge have been incorporated into educational settings.

At the forefront of this specialization spiral the professions can be found, with their accomplishments standing as a banner for all those who would seek society's high rewards of prestige, power, and money. The older professions of medicine, law, and the clergy have long since passed the stage of frantic self-examination in order to earn their places in the sun. The preacher who had a private calling has been replaced by the theological student whose fitness to serve is a matter of collective, as well as private, conscience; the self-schooled individual seeking to take the bar examination is part of another era; the practice of medicine was drastically changed with the passing of the proprietary school.

The increasing importance of the professions in modern industrial societies has led many observers to attempt to express the current *Zeitgeist* in such phrases as "the age of the expert." This development implies that the growth of occupations is based upon specialized knowledge. But it also suggests a concern with the effects of such developments upon education and human values—in short, the cultural consequences. Such concerns make a study of the modern professional mandatory: Who is he? What does he believe in? What is the extent of his influence?

As industrialization and bureaucratization have advanced in American society there has been a parallel development of occupations that claim to have professional status. One of the largest of these new professions is engineering: one out of every fifty males in the labor force in the United States is an engineer. Compared to other professions, engineering has shown a marked rate of growth: the 850,000 engineers reported in the 1960 census represent an approximate

200 percent increase since 1940, twice the growth rate for all professions combined. Future expansion is likely to be equally dramatic, as the present total of 35,000 engineers that graduate annually do not meet the demands of manpower projection studies.[1]

Many of the new and emerging professions have often adopted *the* model set by the older professions in their own search for identification. Such efforts can result in fruitless comparisons between the established and the emerging professions. The emerging professions are obviously different because they developed in different historical periods and therefore incorporated different elements into their structures.[2]

Similarly, the sociological analysis of professions has often imposed the model of the established professions as the measuring rod for newer groups. Such comparisons can, of course, tell us whether or not engineering or other new professions are similar in form to medicine or law, but they tell us little about the relationship between the structure of engineering and the unique demands it faces as an occupation. The sociology of the professions has produced two distinct perspectives of professional occupations. These perspectives are called the "functional model" and the "process model."

The functional model of professions has given central attention to the unifying aspect of a professional education—an education in which both the selection and the socialization of students serve to reduce variability among practitioners. Professions are therefore seen as composed of a relatively homogeneous collection of practitioners who are dedicated to the same professional values, motivated by the same noble goals, constrained by all-powerful professional associations, and who share the same educational and work experiences. In short, the functional model gives special emphasis to the "communal" aspects of professions.[3]

The process model, on the other hand, focuses attention on the developmental stages in the structure of a profession and on internal diversity, with respect to ideology and goals. Professions are thus seen as internally differentiated, with subgroups engaging in power fights involving the nature of the profession and the legitimate activities of its practitioners.[4]

Although these two models are often taken to be incompatible, evidence seems to suggest that both points of view are relevant to a complete understanding of the continuing exigencies that confront professions. There are periods in the history of any profession when dominant ideologies remain unshaken and shape the nature of the profession. Other periods are clearly characterized by divergent points of view and distinct subgroups committed to furthering the objectives of their faction.[5] These considerations apply equally to contemporary professions.

Characteristics of Professions

In spite of the growing number of studies of particular professions and the frequent attempts at theoretical evaluations, the very term "profession" remains elusive. A great deal of confusion is engendered by the loose usage of the term in everyday speech, especially in the distinction between professional and amateur pursuits. The contrast between science or engineering as practiced by nineteenth-century amateurs and as practiced by present-day professionals also suggests more confusion than clarification. There is little reason to assume that the professional of today has greater competence because the contributions of the early giants were clearly great. The obvious difference is that the professional follows his "calling" full time and makes his living at it. Yet, the professional's work is not merely a job; some dedication is implicit in the notion of professionalism, and, curiously, it is the amateur who personifies dedication.

The ambiguity of the term "profession" cannot only be attributed to the accidents of common usage. Despite accusations that the social sciences invent neologisms when ordinary serviceable words would do, most sociological concepts do involve garden-variety English words (which is not to deny that barbaric linguistic transformations are often perpetrated in the name of social science). Seldom, however, does a concept remain as slippery as does the concept of "profession." Perhaps the major reason for this elusiveness is that it is so very highly value laden. It is difficult to think of any social category that bears equal prestige (elites, for example, are not as universally esteemed for they connote something undemocratic). Because the professional model is so highly regarded it tends to be defined somewhat differently by all those who wish to show that their group is a profession.

The complexities of historical change, not to mention those of historical interpretation, further confound the issue. Invariably, the professional model is based upon the three most ancient and established professions—medicine, law, and the clergy—all of which emerged in the medieval world and began to take their present form in the eighteenth century. Interestingly, even these three, epitomizing the "free professions," have their origins in guilds and the ecclesiastical universities, all of whose members were required to take at least minor orders.[6] Accordingly, the idea of a professional as an organization man is not uniquely modern.

The meaning of the term "established professions" is not quite clear. However, no matter what criteria are used, there can be no question that medicine, law, and theology *are* professions. But this is not simply because their genealogy can be traced back into history. Indeed, as Everett C. Hughes has suggested, the search by occupations for a heroic genealogy is merely an act of status seeking, just like the attempt of families to find Mayflower or heraldic origins.[7] In both cases, disreputable skeletons will tend to be ignored, yet these skeletons might well provide the most important clues in tracing evolutionary processes.

Although the term "established professions" seems to connote something more reputable than "new professions," the distinction is invidious. Barber-surgeon ancestry is not intrinsically meritorious. Even if it is agreed that the characteristics of professions are ideals to be emulated, there is no reason to assume that the established professions embody these ideas more fully than do the younger upstarts. It might even be the case that seniority induces sloth, whereas the new arrivals try harder.

If the traditional trinity, upon which the model of the professions is based, had not shared many characteristics, the model could never have been derived. But, should the disparate elements in each receive more attention, it would be more clearly seen that the professional model is a constructed one—an ideal type—and not a description of medicine, law, and theology. The established three did not, from the start, equally measure up to all the criteria of professionalism, and, since their origins, each has altered in innumerable

ways. (University teaching is also an "established profession" by criterion of medieval origins, but it has
received little consideration in comparative analyses
because it departs so dramatically from the medicine-
law-theology model. For example, are philosophers and
astronomers members of the *same* profession?)

The new professions that emerged since the Industrial Revolution—most notably, engineering and various branches of the sciences—need to be considered
in the context of the social processes in which they
arose. To discuss the rise of the technological professions merely in light of technological needs would
be sociologically naïve. Along with changes in the
economic realm, there were major transformations in
the nature of social life. Contemporary life has been
less altered by the machine than it has by the con-
comitant patterns of specialization, urbanization, and
bureaucratization. These forces are taken into account
not only because they explain the proliferation of new
professions in the past century and the increasing size
of professions both old and new, but also because
they give insight into an understanding of the forms
that today's professions have taken. These forces have
not only shaped the new professions, they have also
reshaped the established ones. The one indisputable
trait of the established professions is that they have
been around longer. (Prototypes of both new and old
professions can be found in antiquity, but these resem-
ble modern counterparts only in the functions they
performed as individuals, not as an occupational
group.) Longevity is, however, less likely to explain
current characteristics than is the immediate social
milieu within which the professional is immersed.

Proceeding (hopefully) beyond the looseness of
common usage, not attempting to substantiate the

status claims of any occupation, and not holding any preconceived notions of the differences between the established and the new, the question is asked: What then is a profession?

The most obvious, and misleading, attribute of occupations that are recognized as professions is their prestige. No doubt, because physicians are accorded more prestige than any other occupation, groups aspiring to the magic label of professional attempt to emulate features of the medical world—the doctor appearing as the apotheosis of the professional model. Such blatant status seeking may be rebuffed by bestowers of status because it is so obvious. It is likely to fail for a more interesting reason. Undisputed professional standing is not a consequence of high prestige. Rather, prestige accrues to fields that most clearly embody professional criteria. Unless the status seekers have managed to single out and emulate those features of the medical world that are intrinsic to professional ideas, they may merely be engaged in an absurd parody. White coats do not make a professional.

The essence of the professional model involves a successful claim of authority in an area of exclusive jurisdiction, expertise, or specialized qualifications epitomized in the term *"learned* professions." The knowledge base of the established professions derived primarily from the realm of the sacred—most obviously in the case of the clergy but also in the moral concerns of law and in medicine, which dealt with the mysteries of the human body and life itself. Increasingly, as secular and rational values have become more important, the legitimization of professional work has come to rely upon scientific foundations (even theology is concerned with empirical archeological evidence). The third area that underlies professional work is that of aesthetics.

No profession relies exclusively upon only one of the three realms, although there are considerable differences in emphasis. For example, medicine is, of course, strongly based on science, but it continues to have a major aura of mystery, which the practitioner most likely thinks of as the art of healing. The sciences, in spite of frequently narrow positivistic ideologies, obviously deal with the mysterious and, in the act of creation, have much in common with the arts.[8]

Mystery, which can be penetrated by the use of esoteric skills, affords the creation of professions as a class apart. If the knowledge base for their skills is too broad, it will not readily be recognized as the exclusive license of one community of experts. But such borders are difficult to define—even the most homogeneous appearing professions invariably contain warring segments. A realm of knowledge that is too narrow is also an inadequate source of a professional mandate— it may result in a technique that nonprofessionals can be readily taught. According to Harold Wilensky:

In short, the optimal base of knowledge or doctrine for a profession is a combination of intellectual and practical knowing, some of which is explicit (classifications and generalizations learned from books, lectures, and demonstrations), and some implicit ("understanding" acquired from supervised practice and observation). The theoretical aspects of professional knowledge and the tacit elements in both intellectual and practical knowing combine to make long training possible and to persuade the public of the mystery of the craft. If an occupation is based on knowledge or doctrine which is too general and vague, on the one hand, or too narrow and specific, on the other, it is not likely to achieve the exclusive jurisdiction necessary to professional authority.[9]

An optimal knowledge base is a necessary foundation of professional work, whether the occupation involves service to clients or pursuit of the calling for its own sake, as in science or the arts. Other traits are associated with the knowledge base, but the manner in which they are associated is not always easy to discern. To the extent that the professional possesses a unique expertise, there will be a tendency to develop *autonomy* in the exercise of his skills by rejecting judgments of his performance by outsiders, who, by definition, lack the necessary professional judgment. Autonomy involves freedom to profess their esoteric branch of knowledge and to set standards not only of work but also of training for new entrants. If professional autonomy is part of the practitioner's license, *obligations* are also involved. Professional behavior, like any other, is subject to controls. Because of the unique expertise, the most appropriate source of evaluation and control is not lay, but colleague, professional norms frequently being more stringent than legal ones. The range of responsibility involves not only questions of controls but questions concerning professional goals as well—the latter invariably less clearly defined. Is it part of the scientist's mandate to determine what is done with his product or to concern himself with the common good?

Because of the knowledge base, professions are also characterized by an intensive *commitment*, both in constituting lifelong careers and eliciting strong identification with the work performed (a calling rather than a job). The investment in the necessary long period of professional training makes leaving any pro-

fession unlikely. To the extent that professional schools
not only teach a set of skills but also inculcate professional norms, instilling their inmates with a professional identity, the development of a deep involvement
with the area of expertise and colleagues is inherent
in becoming a professional. Commitment is further
reinforced in subsequent ties with colleagues at work
and in professional organizations.

Each of these characteristics of a profession—
knowledge, autonomy, obligation, and commitment—
are not simply conditions that are present or absent
for an occupation. They are variables, and, as such,
an occupation may be located somewhere on a dimension representing the *extent* to which their knowledge
is abstract and theoretical or the *extent* to which
autonomy is a central concern to the practitioners in a
profession. Moreover, the definition of a profession as
an occupation grounded in abstract, theoretical knowledge, protective regarding the integrity of its expertise, guided by a strong sense of colleague control,
and dedicated to a lifetime of intense activity in a
chosen field can only be taken as an ideal type of
definition that represents the extreme condition of each
characteristic.

Viewed in this way, one profession may exhibit
these characteristics in a different manner than another. The knowledge characteristic, which is probably the least variable of the four, can be used to
classify occupations as more or less professional. Yet,
it is the nature of professional knowledge to have
variations between professionals of different educational cohorts. As abstract, theoretical knowledge
becomes reshaped, new practitioners just out of professional schools may be familiar with the state of
the art that would be quite foreign to their colleagues of

an earlier vintage. Therefore, although the knowledge
characteristic is quite invariant within a small time
span, it is quite variable across several generations of
practitioners.

Autonomy is also a characteristic that will vary
within any profession, especially as work settings
differ. When the medical profession was composed
mainly of independent practitioners who dealt with
clients in a very personal manner, this particular work
experience would be expected to produce very similar views on the importance of autonomy. However,
as the settings in which physicians work shift to
group practice and larger organizational settings, the
importance of autonomy will probably also change in
meaning.

Very much the same thing can be said for commitment and obligation. It is unrealistic to expect all
practitioners of any profession to subscribe to the same
values when their educational experiences, their work
settings, the sophistication and status of their clients,
and their career aspirations and opportunities are so
very different.

Professions and the Social System

There are also broader considerations that are
equally important reasons for studying the professions.
First, there is the role played by the professions in
providing for elements of integration in complex societies; next, there is the importance of the professions in
their direct relation to the emergence of universalistic
standards of judgment in many areas of social life;
and finally, there is the important function of master-
ing the environment for man's benefit. Each of these
reasons is considered in detail below.

One of the characteristics of complex industrial societies is the growth of large social units in which people spend a major portion of their time. The organization and the city have introduced larger elements of rationality and impersonality in social relationships, which are in contrast to the more pervasive communal and kinship ties of an earlier time. Social institutions whose main function is the regulation of relationships between strangers have emerged. This condition of change has put a special strain on social relationships, particularly in those crisis situations that occur in the course of one's life. Whereas such crises as birth, sickness, death, and personal problems were, in communal societies, handled in the context of the intimate communal and primary groups, such sources of support have been less prominent in the urban-industrial society.

How, then, can man in the urban, impersonal society turn to the stranger for the help and support he once obtained from close friends and relatives? How can one learn to trust the stranger in those times of crisis when trust is so crucial? The answer to such questions is not, by any means, simple. Clearly, however, a major role played by the professions in modern society is the *institutionalization of trust* regarding the behavior of the stranger in a situation of crisis. The service ideal espoused by the established and aspiring professions is the basis upon which trust is erected, and normatively supported authority is given to professionals. The development of this element of trust in complex societies is one of the *integrative* functions of the professions.

The importance of this integrative function that is performed by occupational groups was clearly stated by Emile Durkheim some seventy years ago in his work on the division of labor.[10] Durkheim, in his concern over the absence of moral constraints upon economic activities motivated only by self-interest, recognized the important role to be played by occupational groups in establishing moral and ethical constraints upon relationships between employers and workers and between businessmen and customers. He posed the problem in the following manner:

We repeatedly insist in the course of this book upon the state of juridical and moral anomie in which economic life actually is found. Indeed, in the economic order, occupational ethics exist only in the most rudimentary state. There is a professional ethic of the lawyer and the judge, the soldier and the priest, etc. But if one attempted to fix in a little more precise language the current ideas on what ought to be the relations of employer and employee, of worker and manager, of tradesmen in competition, to themselves or to the public, what indecisive formulas would be obtained! Some generalizations, without point, about the faithfulness and devotion of workers of all sorts own to those who employ them, about the moderation with which employers must use their economic advantages, a certain reprobation of all competition too openly dishonest, for all untempered exploitation of the consumer; that is about all the moral conscience these trades contain. . . . An ethic so unprecise and inconsistent cannot constitute a discipline. The result is that all this sphere of collective life is, in large part, freedom from the moderating action of regulation.[11]

In the face of these problems Durkheim found the existing structure of European societies to be incapable of providing the needed relations of solidarity. He said:

To be sure, each of us belongs to a commune, or a department, but the bonds attaching us there became daily more fragile and more slack. These geographical divisions are, for the most part, artificial and no longer awaken in us profound sentiments. The provincial spirit has disappeared never to return; the patriotism of the parish has become an archaism that cannot be restored at will.[12]

What then is to fill the gap left by the weakening of the old social structure? Here is where the critical role of occupational groups is found. As Durkheim said:

A nation can be maintained only if, between the state and the individual, there is intercalated a whole series of secondary groups near enough to the individuals to attract them strongly in their sphere of action and drag them, in this way, into the general torrent of social life. We have just shown how occupational groups are suited to fill this role, and that is their destiny.[13]

These statements by Durkheim on the integrative function of occupational groups are also reminiscent of Thorstein Veblen's vision of the revolutionary role of the engineer in the technological society. Veblen predicted the emergence of a technocracy, with the engineer becoming the guardian of the community's material welfare and who, with his dispassionate, rational mind, would turn the nation's industrial strength and economy out of chaos and onto a path of responsible economic planning. Veblen said:

This industrial system runs on as an inclusive organization of many and diverse interlocking mechanical processes, interdependent and balanced among themselves in such a way that the due working of any part of it is conditioned on the due working of all the rest. Therefore it will work at its best only on condition that these industrial experts, production engineers, will work together on a common

understanding; and more particularly on condition that
they must not work at cross purposes. . . .

Such is the nature of this industrial system on whose
due working depends the material welfare of all the
civilized peoples. It is an inclusive system drawn on a
plan of strict and comprehensive interdependence, such
that, in point of material welfare, no nation and no community has anything to gain at the cost of any other
nation or community. In point of material welfare, all the
civilized peoples have been drawn together by the state
of the industrial arts into a single going concern. And for
the due working of this inclusive going concern it is
essential that the corps of technological specialists who by
training, insight, and interest make up the general staff
of industry must have a free hand in the disposal of its
available resources, in materials, equipment, and man
power, regardless of any national pretensions or any
vested interests.[14]

Since Veblen's writings on the subject, engineering
has indeed become a revolutionary force in society.
Yet, the impact of engineering has had less to do with
the expanded sense of social responsibility that Veblen
foresaw than with the increasing centrality of engineering functions in both developed and developing societies. In the United States engineering has become
the single largest male professional occupation, rapidly
approaching 1 million practitioners. In addition to
growing numbers, recent engineering graduates have
been occupying positions of greater responsibility and
importance than their colleagues of an earlier vintage.
In 1960 over 25 percent of the top 1000 executives of
the 600 largest United States corporations had degrees
in engineering, as compared to only 7 percent in
1900.[15] There is also a marked trend of engineering
employment among more recent graduates in research

and development positions, as compared to earlier graduates' involvement in the more traditional activities of operations, production, and construction.[16]

The decades ahead will find engineers having even greater impact upon American society as they continue to apply scientific knowledge to a wide variety of problems. The Rand Corporation recently conducted an experiment in forecasting the future.[17] The results of the experiment suggest that there will be major efforts in the years ahead in the following: (1) the development of large-scale systems in the development, control, and use of energy and natural resources; (2) continued development of automated manufacturing industries and the emergence of manufactured food to meet the needs of an expanding world population; (3) the development of rapid transportation systems for land, sea, and air; (4) the development of biosocial systems, which are concerned not only with medical advances, housing, community development, and pollution control but also with the coordination of these advances into large-scale social systems, such as the design of cities; and (5) the expansion of space programs and military defense systems. An overriding problem cutting across all these developments concerns the equitable distribution of resources in energy, food, and raw materials that are necessary to cope with expanding population. The stability of government, the lessening of international tensions, and the prevention of future wars may all be closely connected with solutions to the problem of distribution of resources.

These future programs in system design will call for the involvement of engineers on a scale never before seen in the United States or in any other country. The great engineering breakthroughs of the future will be in the development of large-scale technical-social sys-

tems, where the engineers will shoulder responsibility
for many of the nontechnical consequences of technological advances. The significance of these new activities of engineers for the larger society will call for a
profession whose commitment to the idea of social
responsibility will be of vital importance. The established professions of law, medicine, and the clergy
played an important integrative role in society by
institutionalizing a relationship of trust between strangers in crisis situations. However, the established professions have been primarily concerned with the
problems of individuals, and, therefore, their concern
with society has only taken place in the aggregate
sense. Engineering, on the other hand, has been moving more and more in the direction of trying to solve
societal problems by using technological means.
Planned cities, control of air and water pollution, transportation networks, urban education, centralized data
banks, and even crime control have been the subject
of attention by new system analysts.[18] Professional
engineering societies are beginning to establish such
themes for their annual meetings as "Engineering
and the Urban Crisis." (This was the theme for the
1968 meetings of the Indiana Society of Professional
Engineers.) Further examples of this trend are found
in the publications produced and read by system
designers and analysts. The System Development
Corporation magazine has devoted increasing space to
such titles as "The Need for a System Analysis in Welfare," "Automation and Fingerprint Retrieval," and
"Systems Analysis: A Rational Approach to School
Management." [19]

Such efforts directed at the design of complex
technical-social systems will have far-reaching consequences for human values and in the very fabric of

society. The existence of this new technology raises serious questions concerning the net balance of consequences (favorable and unfavorable) in their use. There still are unresolved issues concerning the totalitarian potential of such advanced information systems as centralized data banks, the value criteria to be used in establishing the ends of planned systems and judging their effectiveness, and the increasing autonomy of decision-making systems, which can become impervious to attempts at external control. These conditions will put the integrative functions of the technical-scientific professions to an extreme test. Professionals will have to serve the needs of citizens and society in a manner that creates trusting and cohesive relationships between professionals and their clients.

Closely allied to this integrative function, and at the same time related to the adaptive (that is, economic) functions, is the role of the professions in reshaping the stratification system in industrial society. This influence has occurred primarily in the emergence of new standards of judgment in the evaluation of men. Particularly in the science-based professions, where the values of objectivity and rationality prevail, estimates of individual worth and the distribution of rewards have been strongly influenced by universalistic performance criteria that make rewards available to all who qualify in terms of ability. That such universalistic standards of judgment have permeated the social structure of the larger society is evidenced by the decline in influence of kinship ties, community origins, and social origins. This is not to deny, of course, the still pronounced influence of social, racial, and religious origins upon universalistic standards *within* any particular society. However, viewed in contrast with preindustrial societies, the influence of the professions upon an egalitarian social structure has been very significant.

Along with the processes of industrialization, urbanization, and bureaucratization, there has also been a professionalization of the labor force. As the proportion of occupations that require professional skills has increased, definite shifts in class, status, and power in American society have taken place. William A. Faunce and Donald A. Clelland, in their study of the changing occupational structure of a community, point to "the development of a more cosmopolitan, occupationally based status-assignment system, increasing involvement of professionals in community power structure, and decreased social-class cleavage and identification." [20]

In addition to the normative support for egalitarian social relationships and universalistic standards, the professions have also provided for the existence of numerous high status positions where entry has not been based primarily upon inherited status rules. The notion of "careers open to talent," especially in the salaried professions, has guided the recruitment and careers of many professionals. (Again, there are important variations here, as well as evidence that the professions do not measure up to the ideal that talent should be the main criteria for recruitment and career progress.) This relatively easy entry into elite occupations is a source of social and political stability for any society. A fluid system based upon mobility prerequisites that are shared and potentially available to large numbers of persons provides a basis for integrative bonds among persons who are positioned in various locations in the social structure.

An increase in mobility opportunities has also enhanced the adaptive function of the professions by providing mechanisms for channeling talent into important positions. A large part of economic growth has to do with the development of human resources, as evidenced by the educational level of its population and the nation's ability to absorb its college graduates. Frederick Harbison and Charles A. Myers in their recent work, *Education, Manpower and Economic Growth*,[21] have provided a convincing discussion of the relationship between professional occupations and the social, political, and economic structure of society.

These, then, are some of the important functions of the professions in modern society. But to state these functions is not to explain how they come about. To say that the professions have been important in providing integrative bonds in a complex society that is characterized by increasing impersonality does not explain why such bonds develop. Relations of trust between the professional and his public are largely explained by the very nature of the professions themselves. Thus, in order to understand the functions of the professions described above, one must also understand the characteristics of the professions, because from these characteristics the important societal consequences develop.

At every stage of occupational analysis the professional touchstone is relevant. The initial question is that of *recruitment*, both in terms of quality and quantity. Given the huge demands in terms of numbers, can the quality of recruits meet professional specifications? Given the particular image that the profession has, how does this influence the types of people it attracts? What influence does the orientation of new recruits have upon subsequent development of the profession?

The step beyond recruitment is, of course, profes-

sional *education*—the attainment of esoteric knowledge. Unlike most professions engineering requirements for professional standing are met by an
undergraduate degree. The necessary technical expertise is considerable, and, therefore, the short period of
time in which it is imparted demonstrates remarkable
efficiency. Paradoxically, this efficiency, which is engineering genius at its best, produces effects that have
become of increasing concern to the profession. The
issues are those of breadth of education, depth of
scientific grounding, and social responsibility.

The engineering *career* further shapes, and is shaped
by, both professional and organizational influences. As
a professional employed almost invariably in an organizational setting, the engineer's arena is unique,
as are the challenges for maintenance of professional
standards. As organizations increasingly encroach, the
engineer may embody the model of the professional
of the future. New professional standards and organizational responses will develop in response to this
intercourse.

In order to understand the dynamics of an occupation, it is not sufficient to consider the internal processes of recruitment, molding, and acting-out at work.
The engineer is not only a wielder of a slide rule, but
he is also (gross stereotypes notwithstanding) a social
animal. How do *nonoccupational ties* to family and
community affect him?

The frame of reference for the present study therefore begins with the significance of the professional
in modern society. Then, the depiction of the engineer
proceeds in the context of the guidelines of the fused
functional and process models of professional analysis.
The major focus is, as indicated in the title, upon a
crucial contemporary occupation that, although a

profession, appears to be essentially without a community of shared values, which has been assumed inevitable for professions. Perhaps, above all, it must be noted that although engineering is a new profession, it has by now achieved full public recognition. Nevertheless, it is very much a profession still in process.

NOTES

1. National Science Foundation, *Scientists, Engineers, and Technicians in the 1960's*, NSF 63–64 (Washington, D.C.: National Science Foundation).

2. For a discussion of the importance of time of formation of an organization for determining its structure, see Arthur Stinchcombe, "Social Structure and Organizations," in James G. March (ed.), *Handbook on Organizations* (Chicago: Rand McNally, 1964).

3. William J. Goode, "Community Within a Community: The Professions," *American Sociological Review*, 22 (April 1957), 194–200.

4. See, for example, Rue Bucher and Anselm Strauss, "Professions in Process," *American Journal of Sociology*, 66 (January 1961), 325–334; Harold L. Wilensky, "The Professionalization of Everyone?" *American Journal of Sociology*, 70 (September 1964), 137–158.

5. For some excellent historical materials on this point, see Monte J. Calvert, *The Mechanical Engineer in America: 1830–1910* (Baltimore: The Johns Hopkins University Press, 1967); W. J. Reader, *Professional Men* (New York: Basic Books, 1966).

6. Alexander M. Carr-Saunders and P. A. Wilson, *The Professions* (Oxford: Clarendon, 1933).

7. Everett C. Hughes, "The Study of Occupations," in Robert K. Merton *et al.* (eds.), *Sociology Today* (New York: Basic Books, 1959).

8. Arthur Koestler, *Act of Creation* (New York: Macmillan, 1964).

9. Wilensky, *op. cit.* pp. 149–150.
10. Emile Durkheim, *The Division of Labor in Society,* translated by George Simpson (New York: Free Press, 1947).
11. *Ibid.*, p. 2.
12. *Ibid.*, pp. 27–28.
13. *Ibid.*, p. 28.
14. Thorstein Veblen, *The Engineers and the Price System* (New York: Huebsch, 1921), pp. 52–54.
15. Mabel Newcomer, *The Big Business Executive, 1964: A Study of His Social and Educational Background* (New York: Scientific American, 1965).
16. Robert Perrucci, William K. LeBold, and Warren A. Howland, "The Engineer in Industry and Government," *Journal of Engineering Education,* 57 (March 1966), 237–273.
17. T. J. Gordon and Olaf Helmer, *Report on Long-Range Forecasting Study* (Santa Monica, Calif.: Rand Corporation, September 1964).
18. See, for example, Simon Ramo, "The Systems Approach: Automated Common Sense," *Nation's Cities,* 6 (March 1968), 14–15 and 18–19.
19. *System Development Corporation Magazine,* 9 (May 1966).
20. William A. Faunce and Donald A. Clelland, "Professionalization and Stratification Patterns in an Industrial Community," *American Journal of Sociology,* 72 (January 1967), 350.
21. Frederick Harbison and Charles A. Myers, *Education, Manpower and Economic Growth* (New York: McGraw-Hill, 1964).

2

SOCIAL BACKGROUNDS AND CAREER DECISIONS OF THE ENGINEERING STUDENT

The room was noisy, as the scientists sat themselves at the desks, one or two banging the lids, like a rowdy class at school. Most of them wore open-necked shirts, one or two were in shorts. It struck me that all the top scientists at Barford were present, but none of the engineers. As an outsider, it had taken me years to understand this rift in technical society. To begin with, I had expected scientists and engineers to share the same response to life. . . . The engineers, . . . the people who made the hardware, who used existing knowledge to make something go, were in nine cases out of ten, conservative in politics, acceptant of any regime in which they found themselves, interested in making their machine work, indifferent to the long-term social guesses.

Whereas the physicists, whose whole

intellectual life was spent in seeking new truths, found it uncongenial to stop seeking when they had a look at society. They were rebellious, questioning, protestant, curious for the future and unable to resist shaping it.

This passage comparing engineers and scientists appears in C. P. Snow's novel, *The New Men.*[1] The description of the engineers and scientists contains some of the elements that go into the construction of an occupational stereotype. Yet, such stereotypes, as Theodore Caplow has pointed out, do contain "real" elements.[2] The image of the engineer is often not very flattering, in spite of the current enthusiasm for the realm of science. Scientists and engineers are thought of as rather different sorts of creatures. The glory accorded for accomplishments at Cape Kennedy and in the skies above appears reserved for the men in white coats rather than for their brethren with slide rules (they are usually singled out for "engineering errors" in a space launch). But what of the wielder of the slide rule? Who is he? Is he as pedestrian as his image suggests? Is he, in fact, different from the scientist?

A direct answer to these questions will be avoided and, instead, the assumption that the particular character of any occupation is shaped by three main factors will be entertained. These factors are: (1) the interests, abilities, and social characteristics of those who aspire to enter the occupation; (2) the education or training experiences that serve to provide knowledge as well as identification and values; and (3) the course of a career that provides its own special constraints upon occupational life. In this chapter an attempt to understand the occupation of engineering will begin by taking a close look at the characteristics of those who have chosen to be called engineers.

Social and Intellectual Origins

A notable characteristic of occupational groups that are classified as professions is that the prestige of the profession closely corresponds to the proportions of the practitioners who are recruited from high socioeconomic origins. The proportions coming from professional and white collar backgrounds for various occupations are: medicine—35 percent professional, 44 percent white collar; college faculty—34 percent, 38 percent; law—22 percent, 48 percent; dentistry—27 percent, 43 percent; teachers—17 percent, 29 percent; nurses—11 percent, 27 percent.[3] Comparable figures for engineers indicate that 22 percent are from professional origins and 39 percent are from white collar origins, with the other 29 percent coming from blue collar families.[4] Also, engineers seem to be recruited in much higher than average proportions from families in which the father is a professional, proprietor-manager-farm-owner, or skilled worker. Fewer engineers than would be expected on a probability basis have fathers who are in clerical, sales, semiskilled, or unskilled occupations.

The time trends, with respect to social origins of engineers, reveal that recruitment proportions were fairly stable for sons of professionals, clerical workers, and salesmen. Although sons of proprietors-managers-farmowners are still the largest single category from which engineers are recruited, they showed the sharpest decline in recruitment. Prior to 1940, 36 percent of the engineering graduates were sons of proprietors and managers, whereas in the post-1950 period this proportion declined to 24 percent. An increase in recruitment of the sons of blue collar workers also occurred, with pre-1950 graduates being 70 percent from white collar families and 30 percent from blue collar families, whereas post-1950 graduates were 60 percent from white collar families and 40 percent from blue collar families.

The growing importance and prestige of engineering, which presumably enhances its attractiveness as a career pursuit, has clearly been such as to attract increasing proportions of males from blue collar origins but not those from white collar origins. In fact, recruitment of engineers from professional origins has remained the same despite the growing proportion of the total labor force in professional occupations. This proportion suggests, of course, that engineering is expanding its function as an avenue of mobility for large numbers of blue collar class males. This very important characteristic of an engineering occupation has important implications that shall be examined in some detail below.

In addition to engineers being drawn from selected socioeconomic origins, they are also selectively recruited by geographical region and community size. Over two-thirds of today's engineering graduates were born in the Midwest and the East, which is higher than the percentage of the general population in these areas for any decade from 1920 to the present. The South and the West contribute fewer engineers than would be expected from the population size in these areas.

Engineers also seem to be heavily drawn from rural areas and small towns. Over 25 percent of the engineering graduates were born in rural areas, with another 25 percent coming from small towns with populations of 5000 to 50,000. Engineers born in the 1920s and 1930s were recruited from large metropolitan areas in about the same proportions as the general population distribution for such areas. However, recent recruitment patterns from large cities have not kept pace with expanding urban populations. As the population in large cities approached about one-third of the general population, only about one-sixth of the nation's engineers were recruited from these areas.

These engineering recruits from small communities in the Midwest and the East who are destined to experience considerable social mobility have an additional characteristic in common: they are among the most talented of college students in any discipline. Virtually every study of the ability level of high school students and college students points to the exceptional talents of those interested in engineering careers or those already embarked on engineering careers in college. A study of some 76,000 male college freshmen from 248 colleges and universities indicates that students who chose engineering as their major from among a list of thirty-nine career choices were ranked eighth in their average high school grades.[5] (The same study indicated that engineering students were ranked twenty-fifth in their socioeconomic origins from among the same listing of thirty-nine occupations.) Another national survey of male high school seniors who subsequently attended college indicated that students at the high percentile ranks in measured aptitude are much more likely to choose engineering as their field of study than they are to choose the sciences, mathematics, liberal arts, or humanities.[6]

Thus, the engineering student exhibits three distinctive characteristics. They are of relatively low social origins, or low enough that becoming an engineer will represent an important advance over the social position of their father; they are recruited in sizable proportions from "small town" America; and, finally, they are apparently a talented group of high ability, as indicated by such criteria as high school grades and general aptitude examinations. The particular combination of these characteristics produces distinctive career orientations and occupational values and serves to reinforce, and perhaps establish, certain personality traits.[7] The talented, upwardly mobile student may approach engineering as a career primarily because it offers a clearly visible career line of some prestige and income and not because he necessarily has an intrinsic interest in the occupation itself. (Intrinsic interest in the career may, of course, follow initial attraction.) Another important point is that the rewards of an engineering career can be obtained with a minimum of educational experience. To earn the status of professional in medicine, law, or science, post-baccalaureate education is essential. In engineering the baccalaureate degree alone brings professional status. The educational experience of the engineer is also affected by the mobile orientation toward an engineering career. Often, little time is available for involvement in academic and nonacademic activities in college that are not directly related to the attainment of the engineering degree. Student protests seem like disruptions of vocational timetables. This particular educational experience seems to result from a number of elements, including heavy course loads, little interest in humanities and social sciences by engineering faculty, and, as mentioned above, the essentially vocational orientation toward a career. Many of these points will be examined in this chapter and in the next chapter.

Career Decisions and Occupational Values

Considering the relatively high proportions of engineers from blue collar origins, there is a very early inclination to both attend college and to embark on an engineering career. About 70 percent of a national sample of engineering graduates indicated that they first considered going to college before reaching their junior year in high school, and about 33 percent of the graduates first considered engineering as a career prior to their junior year in high school. Such early career decisions are quite essential for careers that require high school preparation in mathematics and the physical sciences. Chances for a college career in science or engineering would be seriously curtailed if a student did not have a maximum exposure to the sciences and mathematics in high school.

The most influential factors involved in these early career choices are those concerning subject matter interests and career possibilities. When engineering graduates were asked to indicate the importance of a number of factors in their choice of engineering as a career, the factors were cited in the following order:

Interest in science and math subjects

Career possibilities and financial rewards

Work experiences

Hobbies

Reading material on engineering

Discussions with academic advisers in high school or college

Advice from parents

Discussions with faculty members other than advisor
in high school or college

Vocational or similar psychological tests

Friends of own age group

Interest in the subject matter was far above the
others in importance, about two-thirds of the graduates indicated that this was a major source of influence. Interest in career possibilities was a distant
second, one-third indicated that it was very important
consideration in their career choice. In general, the
first two factors in importance represent the split between intrinsic and extrinsic factors in career choice.
This split tends to reappear when looking at the
values and attitudes of practicing engineers, suggest-
ing that it may represent a basic difference in the
reasons for pursuing an engineering career. Influence
from other persons, whether faculty, parents, or
friends, was of relatively little importance in the
choice of engineering as a career. The combination of
an early career choice and a career decision based
upon an interest in the substance of engineering activities or the financial and career possibilities of engineering could lead to an early indifference to all activities that might be considered as distractions from
their main interests. This point may help to explain
why many engineering students have little interest in
the social sciences and humanities, and why they devote little of their time to social and political activities. Possibly, these selective interests develop in
the high school years when their career decisions are
being crystallized and then carry over into their college experiences. The nonengineering, nonscience
areas consist of people-oriented subject matter and
activities that, as will be shown, are not part of the

occupational values considered to be important by engineers. However, this overcommitment to engineering, in the sense of excluding other academic interests, serves to eliminate other fields as competing career possibilities. In a study of occupational choice in college, Morris Rosenberg found that engineering had the smallest amount of occupational turnover (that is, change in occupational choice in undergraduate school) among seventeen occupations.[8] Recently, James A. Davis found that engineering ranked about fifth (of eleven occupations) in stability of career choice as measured by a comparison of freshman career choice and senior field of study of college seniors.[9]

It could be expected from this constellation of early career decisions and exclusive engineering interests that engineering students would be vocationally oriented in college and interested in engineering mainly for its mobility potential. Martin Trow, for example, has pointed to the growing vocationalism in higher education being traceable in part to the mobile orientation of many college students and to the growing rationality and stress upon expertise found in the large society. Engineering students are also thought to exemplify the vocational student subculture, which is characterized by a kind of "off-the-job-training" where ideas and scholarship are often considered to be a luxury and distraction.[10]

Several difficulties involved in this conception of the engineering student serve to reduce the usefulness of such designations as vocational for describing engineers. First, it is not clear whether the alleged vocational anti-intellectual bent of the engineering student is due primarily to those of blue collar origins with a strong mobility drive or is characteristic of the field itself, independent of social origins. A second problem may be that the vocational image of engineering may be a bit dated and out of step with the major changes that have taken place in engineering education over the last decade. The strong science and mathematics foundation in modern engineering has served to recruit students with interests other than those attributed to the traditional "nuts and bolts" engineer. Thus, if engineering students are vocational, they are probably sharing in the general vocational drift in higher education.

A recent study of students scheduled to be admitted as freshman engineers at a large state university attempted to isolate the main reasons the student had for choosing engineering in college.[11] Using factor analysis on items dealing with reasons for going to college, four groups of reasons were delineated. The four groups were intellectual, vocational, traditional, and social. Intellectual reasons were those concerning nonutilitarian career interests; vocational reasons stressed education as being necessary for power, prestige, and money; traditional reasons indicated that persons other than the student urged his college attendance; and social reasons stressed the social-human relations aspect of college life.

The items in each group of reasons are:

INTELLECTUAL

1. I had serious intellectual curiosities that only college could satisfy.

2. I had a compelling interest in one particular field in which I planned/plan to specialize in.

3. I wanted to explore several lines of work to see what I would be most interested in.

4. I wanted to find out more about certain fields of knowledge.

5. I enjoyed studying and wanted to continue academic work.

SOCIAL

1. I hoped to make many new friends in college.

2. I wanted to learn how to get along with people.

3. I thought college life would help me to develop socially.

4. I wanted the close fellowship of living in a dormitory, sorority house, or fraternity house.

5. I hoped that college training would enable me to be a better husband or wife.

VOCATIONAL

1. I wanted to prepare myself for a better paying job than I would otherwise have been able to get.

2. I hoped to acquire some qualifications for leadership in civic affairs.

3. I felt I could live an easier life if I had a college education.

4. I felt college acquaintances and contacts would prove advantageous in finding a position after graduation.

5. I thought a college education would enable me to be more influential in community affairs.

TRADITIONAL

1. It had always been expected that I would go to college.

2. My parents insisted on my going to college.

3. My teachers thought I was good college material.

4. Because vocational and/or similar psychological tests indicated that I would do very well in college.

5. My academic advisers encouraged me quite strongly.

Each student in a sample of 300 incoming freshmen was given a score based upon his responses to the above items, and he was then classified into one of the four main groups. Of these students, 51 percent were classified as choosing an engineering major in college for intellectual reasons; 27 percent for vocational reasons; 17 percent for traditional reasons; and 5 percent for social reasons. Little or no difference was found in reasons for entering engineering for students from upper white collar backgrounds as compared to lower white collar and blue collar backgrounds.

Although this sample is restricted to a single engineering school that may not be typical of the 170 accredited engineering schools in the United States, it does point out that the image of engineering students as having a vocational orientation needs to be systematically examined. They are apparently attracted to engineering because of interest expressed in the subject matter and problems associated with engineering. Thus, if a vocational orientation means an interest in a field because of such extrinsic rewards as prestige, money, and security, then this study indicates that students choosing engineering as an undergraduate field are not especially vocational. However, if by vocational orientation the implication is that the student only has an interest in his own field and has little concern for things outside his area, then engineering students might clearly be considered vocational. But this makes them similar to the large majority of college students in most fields.

Additional factors that cast some doubt on the traditional image of the engineer and cast the engineering profession more in the image of a changing, internally diverse profession are: (1) the changing interests, aspirations, and abilities of engineering students; and (2) the changing patterns of employment for engineering graduates. National surveys cited earlier certainly indicate that significant proportions of the most talented high school students select engineering as their field of study. In addition, such studies noted that interest in graduate study for high school seniors was also found to be most pronounced among the students highest in measured aptitude.[12] A survey of engineering faculty from 156 colleges and universities indicates that in over 85 percent of the schools the interests of appreciable numbers of undergraduate students have shifted to graduate work and research.[13]

The apparent interest of engineering students in graduate work may be a reflection of the changing nature of engineering activities in industry and government and the universities. In the universities there appears to be a growing interest in academic employment among those holding doctorates in engineering. A study of the 1963–1964 recipients of the Ph.D. degree indicates that for the first time a higher proportion of engineers with Ph.D. degrees went into university teaching than did their colleagues in the sciences.[14] Of the engineering graduates, 36 percent went into university teaching, as compared to 29 percent for physics and 23 percent for chemistry. Although the number of Ph.D. holders needed for teaching positions will never be more than a small fraction of all engineers, this new demand does contribute to the growing interest in advanced degree education among engineers.

The employment of engineers in industry and government is moving more and more in the direction of research and development. About 13 percent of the engineers who graduated prior to 1939 had their first job in a research and development function. For those who graduated after 1959 this figure had increased to 32 percent. The corresponding decline for this period was found in employment in operation, production, and construction functions, where the traditional role of the engineer seems to flourish.

Engineering students and practicing engineers seem to be more easily distinguished from those in other fields according to the occupational values to which they subscribe. Clearly, occupational fields differ in the opportunities that they give for the realization of certain personal goals or the satisfaction of certain needs. It is unlikely that a gregarious, "people-oriented" person who is interested in directly helping people would select engineering as his occupational choice. If he did, he would probably either drop out of engineering or lose his interest in people. Because engineering students do much less career switching in college than other occupations, it may be assumed that there is some degree of congruence between the needs of engineering students and the opportunities to satisfy these needs in an engineering career.

In a study of the relationship between occupational choice and social values among college students, Rosenberg identified three value orientations. They are:

PEOPLE-ORIENTED

1. Opportunity to work with people rather than things
2. Opportunity to be helpful to others

EXTRINSIC REWARD-ORIENTED

3. Chance to earn a good deal of money
4. Give me social status and prestige

SELF-EXPRESSION-ORIENTED

5. Permit me to be creative and original
6. Opportunity to use my special abilities or aptitudes[15]

Students in eighteen different occupational fields were asked to respond to the importance that they would give to the three value clusters. Of the eighteen occupational fields, students who planned to enter engineering ranked seventh in the importance they gave to "self-expression-oriented" values (architecture students ranked first in the importance attributed to these values, natural science was fourth, sales-promotion was last); seventeenth in the importance they gave to "people-oriented" values (just ahead of natural science, which was last); and ninth in the importance they gave to "extrinsic reward-oriented" values. Thus, engineering undergraduates were found to express little interest in people and moderately high interest in opportunities for self-expression and attaining money and prestige.

If these same occupational values are used for students choosing their graduate fields, an even better picture of the link between occupational values and career choice can be seen. Because graduate choices imply that a student has already lived with an academic field for four years as an undergraduate student, there should be less in the way of unrealistic choice making reflected in the different fields.

Davis' study of some 33,000 June 1961 graduates

from 135 colleges and universities reported that for
students choosing various graduate fields, engineering
was lowest (of twelve fields) on the "opportunity to
work with people rather than things," highest on the
"opportunity to be creative and original," and third
on "making a lot of money." [16]

Thus, engineers appear to support certain occupational values that are clearly achievable within the
context of their occupation. They are low on interest
in people, high on self-expression, and high on making
money. Some difficulties might be anticipated from the
lack of congruence between little interest in people
and growing involvement in managerial positions during advanced stages of the career. This point will be
discussed again in Chapter 4.

The Freshman Engineer

Perhaps a more revealing picture of engineering
might be obtained by taking a closer look at the neophyte engineer—the young high school graduate who
brings his talents and ambitions to the engineering
school and, in turn, leaves his mark on the character of
engineering in the future.[17]

Intensive interviews with a small sample of freshmen engineers very early in their first semester were
conducted by one of the authors and his research as-
sistant. These interviews were undertaken in order
to understand the interests, motivations, and images of
the incoming freshmen and to estimate the impact of
the "socializing structures" upon the new students.
The students selected for the interviews were also
given a prediction score concerning their probable success in engineering. The prediction equation was
based upon high school rank and scores on the college

board examinations. Students were given a high, medium, or low success potential for the purposes of this study. First of all, four interviews that reflect the range of reasons for selecting engineering and the degree of commitment to engineering reflected in the larger sample of students interviewed have been selected. The first of these interviews is with a student who exhibits a loose commitment to engineering and has a low probability of success; the second student exhibits a moderate commitment with medium success chances in the program; and the last two interviews are with students who have a well crystallized commitment, one having a high success potential and one a low success potential. Each interview was focused upon why they chose engineering as their major field in college.

STUDENT #1: LOW COMMITMENT, LOW PROBABILITY OF SUCCESS

"I don't know. My dad started telling me about it when I was in the seventh and eighth grades, and then in the ninth grade we had this orientation course with files in which there were all sorts of jobs in them. We had to make reports on each job—then we finally got around to filling out—it was just like an application to come here—I guess it was actually the same one they got now. So I signed up for engineering."

"What subjects did you like in high school?"

"Never really cared for math—but I took it every year—got to take it the first two years. My last two years I didn't have to take math, but I took it—I just sort of—well, had to have it. I didn't really like it, but it didn't really bother me. Mostly I got it all figured out and I'd take it to class and it'd be wrong.

I guess what really bothered me most was you'd have to work real long on one problem."

Later on in the first interview we asked again about his occupational choice.

"Well, I always thought about engineering, but really I'm still not sure—I mean I might not even take it next semester. Actually, when I filled out my application—went to the high school counselor—about two weeks straight I think we sat in there and looked at all these pamphlets and stuff, and I never actually was positive I did want to take engineering. So I figured well, it's your freshman year. Everything's pretty much the same any way. So I just signed up for engineering."

STUDENT #2: MODERATE COMMITMENT,
MODERATE PROBABILITY OF SUCCESS

"How did you come to choose engineering?"

"I wish I knew, I really do. [He laughs.] I just figured I liked math and science. Engineering was pretty good. I knew I had to get a degree in something—so —and I wanted to fly an airplane—that's what I wanted to be is a pilot. I just thought aeronautical engineering would be pretty good, you know, so—this is a good engineering school, and mainly the reason that started me out thinking of this school is we lived next to a pilot in Chicago—and he told my father about the technical school they had out at the airport —real good flying instruction. That mainly was what started me thinking about it 'cause they have the best courses for training pilots and technicians."

"Do you need a college education to be a pilot?"

"Oh, yeah. I thought this would be best 'cause usually you need a degree to do anything. What I want to do is just get the degree, and while I'm getting it, probably in my senior year, I'll learn to fly—get the pilot's license—then I'll probably have to go to school for jet training. And then what I want is to get somewhere where I can fly overseas, or something like that."

STUDENT #3: HIGH COMMITMENT,
HIGH PROBABILITY OF SUCCESS

"At first I thought of science. At first it was astronomy about ten years ago. Then chemistry—probably from my brother. My brother had quite a setup. He worked with rockets. Once some material blew up and he had to be sent to the hospital. Well, he thought it was great fun. My brother had some rockets in a science fair project—he worked with solid fuel propellant in missiles. These all failed. But that was a beginning. He's an engineer now, and was in on making the kilotron howitzer shell for the army—that's a nuclear device. And of course we were all very proud. Well, this idea of engineering probably brought me around. After chemistry came physics and math—and electronics now—and the design idea of physics—putting something together from known facts and building something like that. I guess that's about what I want."

"Building something physical or theoretical?"

"This is the question that's in my mind right now. I've always been happy solving mental problems—debating paradoxes in my mind and coming up with good solutions. I'm always proud when I solve or understand a tough math theorem. As a youngster I was interested in mathematical paradoxes—you know, will Achilles catch the rabbit and things like that. Then, on the other hand, I was proud to build and design something. I worked up a battery eliminator for my tape recorder about which I'm very happy. The battle is which do I want to do forever."

"What attracts you about engineering?"

"I guess design—taking concepts and applying them to something practical."

"And to science?"

"Well, I'm still not sure whether it's the design or just the research. I would think I'd probably be happy in both."

In the second interview, the student was still quite certain about electrical engineering, but he was also toying with the possibilities of mathematics and physics. However, he indicates the reason for his initial propensity:

"Because it encompasses such a great deal of my other abilities. For example, my capacity for math, physics, practical application, and my desires in electronics—my background in it as an amateur radio operator, etc. Everything seems to fit in together."

STUDENT #4: HIGH COMMITMENT,
LOW PROBABILITY OF SUCCESS

"In junior high school the counselors tried to help us pick our careers, and we had tests, these punch board tests, and mine came up engineering, and that's what first started my goal, and different years we'd do something like make reports on engineering—broaden our knowledge on it—and, say, in our sophomore and junior years, take field trips to different universities we wanted to attend, and our senior year—most of us applied—we made a trip here."

"What about engineering attracts you?"

"More or less in high school we were mostly, you might say, fed facts, and I know engineering was not all facts—it was mostly theory, and that you were presented with a problem—and you had to use your own knowledge, not necessarily facts—but theory, to work on it more to solve it—and this has always interested me."

"The solving of problems?"

"Yes."

"You could solve problems in other fields. Why this one?"

"Well as a—in my freshman year, I didn't know too much about engineering. I was kind of ignorant of the facts. But then as I investigated and gave my reports, I grew to know more what engineering meant, and what it should mean to other people—and this is what these reports were for—to inform the class about what kind of career you had and what it really meant and we all benefited by it and we just broadened our knowledge and by giving these reports—created interest within yourself to find out more, if you didn't already know it, or things like this."

"Why have you selected aeronautical engineering?"

"Well mostly, as out West—there's missile bases and airplanes like Lockheed and different plants like this I know of. We've had people come and give speeches at the high school to those interested in engineering. They are more or less screaming for engineers, and I figured if I got my degree and probably studied more and extended my knowledge after my degree I may go out there and work."

The first student with a loose commitment to engineering and in the low success potential category dropped out of engineering at the end of the freshman year. He suffered from the additional disadvantage of disliking mathematics, which is critical for the engineering program. The second student had a moderate commitment to engineering as he viewed an engineering degree as essential for his main career objective of becoming a pilot. This student remained in the engineering program at the end of the first year. The third and fourth students both remained in the program, although they differed sharply from the predictions of their success at the beginning of the freshman year.

The new engineering student stands out sharply with respect to his attitudes toward academic subjects outside engineering and science. The general pattern is one of low interest in the social sciences and humanities, although general interest was expressed for these subjects by students in the high predicted success categories. However, the general lack of interest in social science and the humanities seems to be brought to the university from high school, although there may certainly be reinforcement of such views in college. Bringing these high school students together in the same college program undoubtedly leads to a strong student subculture that devalues curricula, activities, and ideas outside their field.

High school seniors preparing to enter college in an engineering program were asked about their interest in subjects outside of engineering. Their responses give a clear indication that they perceive important differences among the disciplines, and they have a strong preference for what they consider to be "tighter," more certain subject matter. All four students quoted below remained in engineering after completing their freshman year.

STUDENT #1

"Physics is an exact science, and when you do an experiment and come out with the results—these are the results you have. Someone else can do the experiment and come out with the same results. I like to analyze a poem, too. But you can take a poem, analyze it, and come out with results—and someone else can read the same poem and get an entirely different interpretation. Now for me to read the poem and to come out with the results, I enjoy it—and I like to hear what someone else does. But as far as pursuing something like this—I prefer something exact. In math, when I come out with the answer, and someone else does the problem—he comes out with the same answer, too. It isn't that English and history don't interest me—but it's sort of the field where everyone has their own opinion—and if somebody else comes out with a new opinion—so what?—he's got his opinion. Whereas in science, you come out with something new—it really is, and you've discovered something."

STUDENT #2

"I enjoy this particular English course, but I get more enjoyment out of chemistry—working out math problems."

"Can you identify what it is you enjoy in one that you don't get in the other?"

"A feeling of accomplishment. In English I suppose I get more of an emotional feeling of disturbance. I'm moody or something—and sometimes I read an English assignment, and sometimes it makes me more moody—and I get an enjoyment out of that—but not a sense of accomplishment."

"What makes for this sense of accomplishment?"

"That I've done this myself. Even after writing a theme, there's no accomplishment. It's fun to know I've written a good theme—but it's no accomplishment. I can't name what it is—it's just when I can clearly understand my way through a problem—I mean understand each step clearly—then I know I've done something."

STUDENT #3

"I do like engineering, but I would enjoy getting a lot more culture than I have, and being able to express myself better, too."

"But if given the choice between the two?"

"Oh, yes, I'd take engineering. I like numbers and I like things that fit. I mean I like everything to go together according to rules and laws. Whereas English, or something like that, it's too much. There's quite a bit left up to the individual. You can interpret things in so many different ways."

STUDENT #4

"Why do you think engineering is more important than the humanities?"

"To me—I'm not interested in humanities. My main interest is engineering. I'm interested in mechanics— taking things apart—seeing what makes them work —and I don't find this in humanities. I'm interested in mechanical things—not government, to take it apart and see what makes them work. Something that's mechanical—it's physical—you can handle it and take it apart and see how it goes together. It's something you can do. But government is so big. You can only talk about it mostly—not much you can do about it."

These statements by future engineering students not only provide some insight into their interest in engineering but also give us some understanding of the personality characteristics of engineering students. These students seem to exhibit considerable concern for order and certainty, as compared to the ambiguity of disciplines where everyone's opinion is equal. This is, of course, a faulty view of the humanities and social sciences, for such disciplines also carry well established criteria for evaluating performance. The crucial distinction seems to be the engineer's strong "activistic" orientation toward what he does. He wants to see things work, put in motion, and tested in the real world, not in the logical world. Activism, in combination with a low tolerance for ambiguity, may provide some of the essential characteristics that motivate students to enter engineering. What appears to us as a low tolerance for ambiguity may possibly be nothing more than low tolerance for activities that distract them from their degree objective or from their work in engineering.

The strong mobility orientation of engineering students, which was described earlier, may help to explain the peculiar connection between the origins of engineers and their career interests and personality patterns. For example, because many engineering students come from social and economic origins in which college attendance is not the modal pattern for high school males, they are obviously different from their teen-age blue collar class peers. Certainly they are much more talented, but talent may not be enough for the blue collar class male to make it to college. Because he probably receives less encouragement for college from his social environment than does the white collar class male, it is possible that talent must be combined with an exceptionally high drive to achieve certain goals. This drive is essential because it is his major resource in the attainment of goals, and a high drive could lead to an exclusion of all other activities and interests that interfere with the major goal. Thus, the very characteristics that are essential for his recruitment to engineering also serve to produce those characteristics of engineering students often regarded as less than desirable.

In this same connection the lack of interest in people exhibited by engineers can be understood. For, if engineering students come from an environment where college attendance is not the norm, it would suggest that male adolescents who are fully integrated into the adolescent culture would also not be interested in college. Thus, engineering students who come from such a setting may have been able to leave precisely because they had loose ties with their peers and adults. If they were more people-oriented, they would never have had the psychological resources to consider a college education and an engineering career.

Thus, the engineering student and the engineer can emerge from outdated stereotypes if we begin to examine the forces at work in his recruitment, his education, and his career.

NOTES

1. C. P. Snow, *The New Men* (New York: Scribner, 1954).
2. Theodore Caplow, *The Sociology of Work* (Minneapolis: University of Minnesota Press, 1954), pp. 134–137.
3. See, for example, Douglas M. More, "A Note on Occupational Origins of Health Service Professions," *American Sociological Review*, 25 (June 1960), 403–404; Stuart Adams, "Trends in Occupational Origins of Physicians," *American Sociological Review*, 18

(January 1953), 404–409; Stuart Adams, "Origins of American Occupational Elites," *American Journal of Sociology*, 62 (January 1957), 360–368; W. W. Charters, Jr., "The Social Background of Teaching," in N. L. Gage (ed.), *Handbook of Research on Teaching* (Chicago: Rand McNally, 1963), Chap. 14.

4. For details on the social, geographical, and intellectual origins of engineers, see Robert Perrucci, William K. LeBold, and Warren A. Howland, "The Engineer in Industry and Government," *Journal of Engineering Education*, 57 (March 1966), 237–273.

5. Charles E. Werts, "Career Choice Patterns: Ability and Social Class," *National Merit Scholarship Corporation Research Reports*, 2, 3 (1966).

6. John C. Flanagan *et al.*, *Project Talent: The American High School Student*, Research Project 635 (Pittsburgh: University of Pittsburgh, Project Talent Office, 1964).

7. In this connection, see Martin Trow, "Some Implications of the Social Origins of Engineers," in *Scientific Manpower* (Washington, D.C.: National Science Foundation, 1958).

8. Morris Rosenberg, *Occupations and Values* (New York: Free Press, 1957).

9. James A. Davis, *Undergraduate Career Decisions* (Chicago: Aldine, 1965), p. 15.

10. See, for example, Martin Trow, "The Campus Viewed as a Culture," in H. T. Sprague (ed.), *Research on College Students* (Boulder, Colo.: Western Commission for Higher Education, 1960); Martin Trow, *op. cit.*, "Some implications . . ."

11. Graham C. Kinloch, "Commitment, Expectations and Experience: A Study of Engineering Freshmen" (unpublished M.S. thesis, Purdue University, 1966).

12. Flanagan, *op. cit.*, pp. 5–59.

13. William K. LeBold *et al.*, "Educational Institutional Views of Undergraduate Goals of Engineering Education," *Journal of Engineering Education*, 56 (February 1966), 213–227.

14. Research Division, National Education Association, *Teacher Supply and Demand in Universities, Colleges, and Junior Colleges, 1963–64 and 1964–65*, Research

Report 1965–R4 (Washington, D.C.: National Education Association, April 1965).

15. Rosenberg, *op. cit.*, Chap. 2.

16. James A. Davis, *Great Aspirations* (Chicago: Aldine,
1964), pp. 172–185.

17. Data in this section have been obtained from Richard
J. Wunderlich, "The Freshman Engineer: A Study
of Occupational Commitment" (unpublished M.S.
thesis, Purdue University, 1965).

3

EDUCATION AND PROFESSIONAL SOCIALIZATION

The primary purpose of the professional schools in American universities is to transmit formally a body of expert knowledge that will enable the professional to practice his skills at an acceptable level of competence in the larger society. A secondary purpose, which, although equally important to the first, is not always acknowledged because it is achieved not through formal instruction but through contact with faculty and peers, is the transmission of values, attitudes, and commitments that will serve to bind the novice to the profession. The pursuit of these ends results in characteristics that are particular to the professional school and that are generally not found in undergraduate education and in many of the nonprofessional graduate programs. The first of these special characteristics is the close connection between the educational activities of the professional school and the larger society in which its graduate will practice. Professional associations maintain close ties with the professional schools, as do the employers of professional talent, especially the large-scale organizations. Curriculum matters may be less bound by tradition than by the utilitarian standards of the marketplace. The second characteristic is the importance attached to maintaining faculty who have had experience as practitioners outside of their academic roles. The third characteristic is the fact that the professional schools tend to isolate their students from the larger university community by providing a separate curriculum. This structural arrangement serves to help attain the professional school's goal of having its students develop common career identifications and commitments. It also tends to encourage the physical and psychological distance that one often finds between the students and faculty of the professional schools and those of the larger university community. The beginnings of the "oppositional and separatist" cultures of the university may perhaps be traced to the structural arrangements that serve to minimize contact in the university community.

Engineering schools are found to share these characteristics with medical schools, law schools, and seminaries. However, the engineering profession seems to experience certain of these characteristics in a more extreme or magnified form than do any of the other established professions. Engineering is alone among the more established professions in conferring professional status upon persons with only the baccalaureate degree. Law, medicine, and the clergy require their students to complete what is essentially a preprofessional liberal education. The "narrowness" of the professional training is less of a problem when there has been a preprofessional educational experience. In engineering education the baccalaureate program must be devoted to both a general liberal education and a specialized professional education. Thus, many more engineering students than students in the more established professions are subjected to multiple and burdensome demands on their academic time. Professional education is often undertaken by engineering students before they may have developed a special commitment. Without the very effective screening device of preprofessional education, attrition rates in engineering schools are much higher than those found in law, medicine, and the clergy. High attrition rates in this case can be attributed to both poor academic performance and uncrystallized career commitments.

The second aspect of the engineering profession that is not generally found in other professions is the great diversity in professional education, work activities, and engineering societies. These differences serve to fragment the profession. There are approximately 250 institutions in the United States that award a baccalaureate degree in engineering, with about 170 of these programs formally accredited by engineering education. Circling this dominant pattern of the four-year baccalaureate degree, five-year programs for the baccalaureate, evening school programs, and work-study cooperative programs can be found. In these programs degrees are awarded in over twenty-four engineering specializations, although the large majority of degrees are awarded in civil, chemical, electrical, and mechanical engineering.

All this takes place at schools that provide curricula with different emphases on science, mathematics, technology, engineering science, and the humanities. Hourly requirements for the baccalaureate degree at these engineering schools range from a low of 120 semester hours to a high of 188 semester hours. In 1965 this extraordinarily diverse educational program awarded approximately 36,700 baccalaureate degrees, 12,000 master's degrees, and 2100 doctorate degrees.

Changing Patterns of Engineering Education

Yet, perhaps the greatest source of diversity in engineering programs has been the result of changes in the content of curricula over the last half century. Since the time when it first emerged in the early nineteenth century in connection with the growth in rail and inland water transportation, engineering has moved from an occupation based upon on-the-job training to a profession requiring advanced educational degrees. During this period it has also moved from being essentially an art, epitomized by the practical inventors of the nineteenth century, to a discipline, firmly grounded in mathematics and the physical sciences. This development is by no means complete, as many practicing engineers are still without formal academic credentials and an overwhelming number have only the baccalaureate degree.

The great changes in engineering education are easily documented by the large-scale studies of engineering education undertaken by various engineering societies in the twentieth century. In 1918 a study of engineering education reaffirmed the then current role of engineering as an essentially practical activity based more on providing educational situations analogous to industrial experience than on the basic sciences.[1] This report stressed the role of the laboratory, industrial training, and shopwork as essential in the undergraduate program. In this same vein cooperative education programs providing for time at school and in industry were also recommended. Serious doubts were raised in this report as to whether or not a student's performance in mathematics and science should be used as criteria for judging ability to do engineering work. This report clearly shows that science had not yet had its impact upon engineering activities, which were still very much shaped by industrial experience. This point is very convincingly underscored by the fact that in 1900 the Bureau of the Census indicated that there were some 43,000 engineers in the United States, whereas statistics on higher education indicate that in the same year only about 1000 degrees were awarded in engineering. Engineering was unquestionably in the hands of the practical men without formal degrees in their field.

Between 1926 and 1930 a series of reports were released in engineering journals as part of a comprehensive study of engineering education.[2] In these reports central attention was given to engineering curricula and to the selection and education of engineering students. One of the reports of this study explored the merits of unified curricula versus divided curricula (unified curricula are for a single engineering degree rather than degrees in different engineering fields and are more likely to be supported by engineering educators than by industry), considered the possibility of extending the length of the undergraduate education

period, and discussed the developing place of graduate study in engineering.

In the period immediately following World War II,
two studies of importance were undertaken by engineering societies.[3] The first study, released in 1944,
gave considerable emphasis to humanities and social
studies to parallel the scientific-technological basis
of engineering. As stated in the report: "Undergraduate curricula should be made broader and more
fundamental through increased emphasis on the basic
sciences and humanistic and social studies." The second report was unique in that it was devoted entirely
to graduate study in engineering. It pointed to the
emergence of a specialized body of engineering knowledge that justified graduate study in engineering as
distinct from graduate study in the physical sciences.

The final major study of engineering education—
the Grinter report, which had the greatest impact
upon curricula—was conducted in the early 1950s and
released in 1955.[4] The basic sciences, mathematics,
and the engineering sciences were recommended as
the basis of engineering education. This can be viewed
as the culmination of efforts to move engineering from
a practical art to a science-based profession that is
concerned primarily with the functions of research,
development, and engineering design.

Each of these major studies has effected important
changes in the curricula of engineering schools and
in the role of engineering in the larger society. As
these changes were put into operation, many thousands of engineers were educated with different bodies
of formal knowledge and different conceptions of the
whole engineering enterprise than their colleagues of
an earlier vintage. These rapid changes resulted in
the creation of tremendous diversity among engineer-

ing practitioners who do not differ as much by age as by years since college graduation. Such diversity can function to set engineer against engineer on issues dealing with engineering education and the engineering profession. In the early 1900s the major split developed between engineers with a college degree—who were in a minority—and the nondegree engineers already with considerable experience.

In the mid-1950s, when engineering schools were graduating between 30,000 and 40,000 persons a year, a split was established between the experienced engineers of the so-called nuts and bolts variety and the new graduates, who were well grounded in the physical sciences, mathematics, and computer sciences. In each case, the lines were drawn between those with experience and those with new knowledge. The experienced engineer was most likely to hold positions of authority in industry and also to hold important controlling offices in engineering societies. The young graduate, with his bright, shiny new knowledge, was in great demand in industry, but he found himself in subordinate positions to engineers whom he considered less knowledgeable than himself. The engineering societies, with the power to influence the future direction of the profession, were also controlled by the experienced graduates of an earlier era.

A concrete manifestation of the internal differentiation in the engineering profession based upon knowledge and expertise can be found in the salary data on engineers and in the engineers' concern over the problem of technical obsolescence. A graph comparing salary against experience indicates that engineers have a sharp salary increase in the years following college graduation followed by a "flattening" and slight decline in the curve for those with twenty and more

years of experience.[5] The existence of different educational cohorts accounts for this variation. Similarly,
engineering literature stresses the great concern over
the problem of technical obsolescence. Many have
suggested that after seven to ten years engineers become "out of date." This is more a comparative statement regarding engineers graduated prior to the new
science-mathematics curricula of the mid-1950s and
those graduated after such curricula were put in
effect.[6]

Thus, the education of engineers in the twentieth
century has produced great diversity in technical
knowledge and in conceptions of the engineering
profession. The graduates of the last decade are different from their colleagues of an earlier vintage. The
engineer-scientist did not exist over a decade ago, and
he is sometimes so different that he may find himself
without an established "home" in either engineering
or science. An equal force producing diversity in the
profession can be traced to the varied needs of the
many industries in which engineers are employed.
Industry is able to make its views known to engineering educators through their affiliations with the American Society for Engineering Education (ASEE).
Industry is represented in the ASEE through a formal
arrangement of the Industrial Members of ASEE.
Each member organization provides a representative
whose main function is to work with educators concerning matters related to the education of engineers.
In such matters industry is kept informed of new
developments in engineering education that may affect their particular industry, and a means is provided
whereby the needs of industry can be communicated
to educators. This is, of course, the way in which professional schools are informed of the performance of

their graduates in the larger society and whether or not there is a good "fit" between the educational program that is provided and the work activities that the new graduate will be expected to perform.

The particular needs of industry for engineers with certain educational preparation are quite varied. Providing a single educational program at the baccalaureate level that will prepare engineers for the varied work functions in which they will be employed is very difficult. In the face of such diversity in types of engineers, the ASEE has encouraged greater flexibility in the engineering schools than would be found in the medical and law schools. Some schools have adapted to this flexible philosophy by providing an educational program that is geared to the needs of a local or regional industry, whereas others have prepared their graduates for national needs or for advanced degree programs. Engineering schools have also differed in their emphases on certain curricula and in their maintenance of specialized, as compared to unified, undergraduate programs.

The development of quite diverse educational programs to meet the varied needs for engineering graduates would appear to be one of the strengths of engineering education. Because the demand for engineers has generally exceeded the supply, the "loose" control of the professional schools has not resulted in a "flooding" of the labor market with engineers trained in areas for which there is little demand. However, although this diversity has been a strength vis-à-vis the employment of engineering graduates, it has had a negative effect upon the emergence of a unified engineering profession. Just as the previously discussed historical changes in engineering education have led to great differences among engineering graduates in different periods, so have the diversity of present-day educational programs led to differences among engineering schools and the graduates from these schools.

The numerous educational programs found in the engineering schools, which have emerged both by design and by evolutionary changes, can be reduced to more manageable dimensions by considering the consequences of these programs for the needs of industry. Undergraduate engineering education seems to serve three major functions in terms of the needs of industry. The first function is engineering education as a basic education in a scientific-technological society. A considerable number of organizations in different industries that employ engineers seem to view the engineering graduate as a person well grounded in the basic sciences and mathematics and thereby suited for a large number of positions in their organizations. Many of the larger organizations employing thousands of engineering graduates provide their own training programs, which serve to focus the educational knowledge of the engineer upon the specific products of the organization.

A top management representative of a large research-oriented manufacturing organization expressed his view of engineering education as one that prepared persons to perform many activities. He said, "Our experience over a span of years, and with continually more complex technological challenges arising in the various engineering fields, is that the Bachelor of Science degree in engineering represents an adequate and firm educational foundation—producing a professional graduate who is broadly capable of functioning in a wide variety of the many entry-level jobs that exist and will exist in industry. It is a foundation adequate to build on for further professional growth whether that growth be in graduate academic work or advanced industrial responsibilities."

This view of engineering education as a basic education in a technological society is also maintained by many educators who have noted how the focus in higher education has shifted away from the liberal arts colleges to the professional schools and the schools of science.[7] The changing nature of the economy has made higher education a critical resource for continued economic growth, with the result that higher education has become much more than a means to personal growth and disinterested pursuit of knowledge. Under such changes the traditional "liberal arts" degree may be less suited as a national resource than a "liberal science" degree. Thus, engineering education as a basic education in a scientific-technological society would be taken by many students as a general curriculum and not necessarily as preparation for professional practice in engineering.

The second function of the engineering school is to produce graduates for immediate productivity in industry at the completion of the baccalaureate degree. The educational program in such schools is likely to select courses in the curriculum according to their usefulness in meeting the needs of a clearly delineated set of work activities. Advanced courses in mathematics, the physical sciences, and the engineering sciences may be neglected in favor of courses in specific technologies that are closely related to one's specialization as a mechanical engineer or an electrical engineer. Graduates from such programs readily adapt to the technical requirements of their position and require little on-the-job training. The comments of a top management representative in an organization that is primarily interested in engineers with baccalaureate degrees who have course preparation in areas directly related to their production needs pointed out that many of the recent engineering graduates have so much general theory and advanced mathematics that they are of little value when they first join the organization. He indicated that such graduates must often be supervised by experienced technicians who can show them how to do the many detailed things that are ordinarily taught in shopwork-type courses.

In such industries there is an image of the engineer as the type of person "who can roll up his sleeves and get down on the floor and make something work." Such engineers clearly do work on "things" and, as such, must be familiar with all the inputs that make these "things" work and keep them working. However, the enginering graduate with more exposure to the physical and engineering sciences and mathematics has been trained to work on solutions to problems rather than concrete operating systems that produce a product. Their product is often a paper report that is designed to help someone else build and operate a concrete structure or machine.

The third function of undergraduate engineering education is to prepare the student for advanced study in engineering that will lead to higher degrees. This function has emerged in response to the growing need for engineers with advanced degrees and to a changing conception among some educators and professional societies that full professional status for engineering graduates can only be obtained with advanced degrees. A study of national manpower needs undertaken by the President's Science Advisory Committee (at the request of President Kennedy) indicated that in 1970 the number of doctorate degrees awarded in engineering, mathematics, and physical sciences should reach

7500 and the number of students with a full year of study beyond the baccalaureate degree should reach 30,000.[8] These objectives will probably not be achieved in light of current enrollment figures in the graduate schools. Despite the fact that between 1955 and 1965 the number of master's degrees awarded in engineering increased by 169 percent and doctor's degrees increased by 251 percent, the number of graduates is still below projected needs.

The role of the advanced degree as a criterion for professional status is reflected in the *Preliminary Report* issued by the most recent study of engineering education undertaken by the ASEE.[9] The first two recommendations of this report are:

1. The *first professional degree* in engineering should be the master's degree, awarded upon completion of an integrated program of at least five years duration. This degree should be uniformly identified as the Master of Engineering degree, without qualifying adjectives or phrases. It is expected that implementation of this recommendation can be accomplished within a period of five to seven years.

2. Four-year bachelor's degree programs leading to an *introductory engineering degree* should continue to be offered.

Both of these recommendations are designed to establish a preprofessional degree at the baccalaureate level and to have the first advanced degree be the professional degree. The response to several of the recommendations of the *Preliminary Report* (including the two mentioned above) clearly revealed divisions among both educators and industry people in the conception of the engineering enterprise and in the curriculum required to educate engineers.[10] A frequent criticism of these recommendations is that the baccalaureate degree would be downgraded and the several hundred thousand engineers with only a bachelor's degree would be reduced to a subprofessional status. This battle is a familiar one that is often faced by occupations making claims to professional status. Sometimes it is a battle to prevent the practice of a particular set of activities by persons without formal training, and sometimes it is a battle to require additional education as a means to attain full status as a professional.[11] In each case there is a threat of either loss of occupation or loss of prestige, which is certainly enough to make such struggles long and bitter.

The three functions of undergraduate engineering education—basic scientific-technological education, education for immediate productivity, and preparation for advanced study—have some degree of support in the engineering schools, in industry, in professional societies, and among practicing engineers. All this diversity of educational programs coexisting at the same time is a relatively recent phenomenon. Prior to about 1955 undergraduate engineering education was largely dominated by the function of providing graduates for immediate productivity. Coinciding with the Grinter report, increasing strength was given to the other two functions of engineering education, although they still do not dominate the majority of schools and industries. Over 400,000 engineers have graduated since 1955, and the large majority of advanced degrees have been awarded in engineering since that time. Possibly, ten years were necessary to develop support for the new functions of engineering education. As large numbers of graduates with the science-mathematics curricula were produced by engineering schools, they were more likely to be employed in research and development functions and in organizational settings that encouraged and demanded advanced degrees of their engineers. During this ten-year period engineering graduates with more of an inclination to support the idea of engineering as an advanced degree program were probably moving into positions of some influence in engineering schools, organizations, and professional societies.

Yet, the balance between these different views of undergraduate engineering education is very much a dynamic and changing matter. At the present time there seems to be close to equal support for engineering education both for immediate productivity and as preparation for advanced study (including engineering education as a basic liberal science education) About one-half of the practicing engineers in industry and government agree with the view that a bachelor's degree was sufficient preparation for their work and that graduate work was not necessary. A little over two-fifths of the management representatives from a national sample of organizations employing engineers held the same view of the educational needs of those engineering graduates employed in their organizations. About two-fifths of the management representatives also indicated that a specialized undergraduate curriculum, as compared to a common curriculum, was best suited for the needs of their organization. The advantages, as seen by these organizations in the specialized program, are that it facilitates recruitment of new graduates and limits the need for on-the-job training programs that would be costly and time consuming. Additional complexity and diversity occur because there is considerable variation among industries concerning support for these two types of curricula. The strongest support for the common program is in research and development, utilities, electrical equipment, and aerospace industries. Strongest support for the specialized program is in construction, local government, and engineering and architectural services.

Some changes that should serve to upset this balance between the principal functions of engineering programs are currently in motion in engineering education. The two most important are the emergence of technical institutes that offer a two-year associate degree as an engineering technician and the establishment of baccalaureate degree programs in engineering technology. Manpower planners in a national sample of organizations employing engineers indicate that over one-third of the organizations had an inadequate supply of technicians and over three-fourths projected a need for increasing numbers of engineers in the future. As many as one-fifth anticipated that twice as many engineers would be necessary. A National Science Foundation study projected a need for approximately 1.5 million engineers by 1970.[12] If, as some have suggested, the economy needs about two to four engineering technicians for each engineer or scientist, then the production of formally educated technicians is falling short of the need. In 1964, for example, there were 14,471 associate degrees awarded in engineering technician programs whereas some 43,000 engineering degrees were awarded. Enrollments in technician programs are also sizable and show a continuing growth pattern. A report on 177 institutions that offer such programs indicates that enrollments increased from 57,589 students in 1963 to 65,731 students in 1964, an increase of 14 percent.[13]

The baccalaureate degree programs in engineering

technology, which have also appeared on the national scene, are designed for students whose responsibilities will lie between those of the professional engineer with an advanced degree and the semiprofessional engineering technician with a two-year associate degree. A recent study by Jesse J. Defore indicates that seventy-three institutions currently offer four-year engineering technology degrees and that most of these programs are relatively recent in origin.[14] The academic administrators of the seventy-three programs indicated that "requests from industry" and "perceived student needs" were the major reasons for the emergence of the programs. Among the specific industry needs that influenced these programs is the view that "undergraduate engineering education has tended to become more science-oriented, the focus for professional education has shifted to the graduate level, labor and industrial leaders have special needs for the 'practical' engineer, and modern technology is becoming more and more complex with many new areas of specialization . . ."[15]

Defore also described the comparison between the established engineering program and these two new programs. He said:

As compared to four-year engineering programs, baccalaureate engineering technology programs tended to concentrate more on technological methodology, to be more flexible, to contain less science-related subject matter, and to require fewer total credits for the degree. As compared to associate degree engineering technology programs appeared less intensive, required a smaller proportion of their total credits in the technical areas, and had a larger proportion of the total requirements in the curricular area which included unrestricted electives.[16]

The full impact of these new programs upon more established engineering programs is still to be felt. The impact is expected to have far-reaching effects on engineering enrollments, advanced degree education, and employment patterns in industry. The engineering technology programs are clearly designed to produce the type of engineer who will "roll up his sleeves" and who wants to work with physical, rather than mental, constructions. Such programs should tend to recruit the many students who are attracted to engineering because of the strong instrumental impulse to get things working and who may have a low tolerance for the more theoretical materials in engineering science, physical science, and mathematics, where the link between the curricula material and future work activities is not always clear to the student. Students without the interests or resources for graduate study will also be more likely to choose engineering technology programs. The lower credit hour requirement in the technology programs may also be an inducement for persons who wish to complete their studies in four years. Although the regular engineering programs are designed for completion in four years, a very high percentage of students need an extra semester to complete the program because of the demanding nature of the courses in both number and content.

With this streaming of students into technology programs, the remaining students who select established engineering programs at the undergraduate level would perhaps be more interested in graduate study, better prepared in science and mathematics from their high schools, and of sufficiently comfortable economic origins to make full-time advanced study possible. All this should serve to increase the chances that professional status in engineering will be restricted to these persons with at least a master's degree and, some have even suggested, perhaps the doctorate. The emerging pattern would be one of a preprofessional undergraduate program and specialized professional training at the graduate level. This, of course, will not take place without a good deal of battling within the engineering "community". Time is necessary for the number of advanced degree engineers to be large enough to make a struggle for control of engineering education possible. Another possibility—and one that would be detrimental for the development of a single engineering profession—is that the advanced degree engineer will be given a special designation, such as the engineer-scientist. The result would be greater fragmentation of engineering and limited influence for engineers with advanced degrees.

In industry, the new distributions of power, prestige, and income that follow the new engineering programs would also contribute to the changing character of the engineering profession. A significant percentage of engineers with baccalaureate degrees seems to be employed in work functions and engaged in work activities that are subprofessional in nature and better suited to the talents of a technician or technologist. Some engineering graduates are simply being underutilized. The graduates of associate degree programs and technology programs will tend to compete with many of the graduates of established engineering programs for the same positions. This would tend to put pressure on the traditional four-year engineering programs as many of their graduates would be receiving similar work positions and rewards for an educational program that is more demanding and takes longer to complete. Thus, there would be an additional in-

fluence to encourage high school students interested
in engineering activities to move into technician and
technology programs rather than into engineering
programs.

In general, then, the many changes in engineering
education in this century seem to have created different educational generations of engineers who are
often widely dissimilar in the character of their education, their formal degrees, their work activities,
and their views on the engineering profession. Other
factors leading to segmentation of engineering are
found in the patterns of contemporary education programs and in the varied needs of industry for engineering graduates with different abilities, interests,
and qualifications. The presence of such diversity and
segmentation reveals very vividly that a profession
cannot be adequately understood within a static framework that stresses the unanimity among professionals
on matters related to education and practice. An understanding of the competing and conflicting interests
within the profession, and within that part of the larger society that is organized to use the services of
that profession, provides a revealing picture of the
internal dynamics of the profession and of the forces
leading to further diversity or unity in the profession.

Education and Employment

As mentioned earlier, one of the roles of the professional school is to ensure that only persons with that
specialized education are able and allowed to perform
the special activities of the profession. Harold L.
Wilensky has discussed this as "exclusive jurisdiction"
and claiming a monopoly on a particular skill.[17] An
additional characteristic is that the specialized pro-

fessional training is only preparation for a single occupation and that particular occupation becomes the
terminal occupation in one's career.[18] Yet, a National
Opinion Research Center report on the Post-Censal
Survey of professionals indicates that not all holders
of engineering degrees are employed as engineers
and that many persons holding degrees in other areas
are employed as engineers.[19] Of those who received
degrees in engineering, only 58 percent of the bachelor's degree recipients, 57 percent of the master's
degree recipients, and 80 percent of the doctorate
degree recipients were employed as engineers. A career commitment to the field, which is essential for
the stability and growth of a profession, is clearly
much more characteristic of the doctorate engineer
than his colleagues without the doctorate. Almost one-
third of the engineers with the baccalaureate degree
were found to be employed in nonengineering positions, such as craftsman and foreman; manager, official,
and proprietor; and sales, clerical, and kindred workers.

Over 60 percent of those who received a baccalaureate degree in physics are employed as engineers.
The percentage drops off sharply—25 percent of the
physicists with a master's degree and 9 percent of
the physicists with a doctorate degree are employed
as engineers. Less than 10 percent of degree holders
in mathematics and statistics and in chemistry are
generally employed as engineers.

Although it cannot be determined from these data,
it would be important to know the particular point in
the career that engineering graduates left engineering
for other occupations. For example, a much higher
percentage of engineers with bachelor's degrees might
be employed as engineers immediately following col-

lege and in the early stages of their career and then
shift out of engineering much later in their career.
Earlier, a discussion of the differences between the
educational generations as being due to the major
changes in engineering education was presented. Considering that discussion, a hypothesis can be made:
movement out of engineering is associated with technical obsolescence. That is, one adaptation to the loss
of formerly held skills or to the failure to keep abreast
of new developments in one's field is to change careers. If this is the case, a modification of Wilensky's
previously discussed hypothesis is suggested. While
Wilensky said that in order for an occupation to maintain a monopoly on its practice, the character of its
knowledge must "neither be too vague nor too precise,
too broad nor too narrow," [20] we would add the idea
that the character of the knowledge should also allow
the professional to keep himself up-to-date by self-
education programs. This would serve to reduce any
career switching that might be due to technical obsolescence.

In addition to the fact that career switching serves
to reduce the extent to which an occupation takes on
characteristics of a profession, there can be switching
within the profession itself, which also takes place at
later stages in the career that may function in the
same way. A comparison of the field of study of engineers at the undergraduate level and the field in
which they are presently employed gives some indication of the extent of field shifting that takes place
between the period of formal education and of employment. Over 80 percent of those who graduated in
civil, chemical, electrical, and mechanical engineering
are still employed in their same field. Metallurgical
and mining engineers lose about one-third of their

graduates to other fields during employment, whereas over one-half of the aeronautical and industrial engineering graduates have moved out of their field of graduation for employment. Only one in ten of the engineering science graduates indicated that their current employment was in engineering science.

Thus, the engineering profession seems to experience difficulty in maintaining control over its practitioners due to its inability to maintain exclusive jurisdiction over their activities and due to extensive attrition. Both the name and position of engineer seem to be easily appropriated and discarded. In addition, the field switching that does take place among engineers between graduation and employment is probably the result of such factors as degree of curriculum specialization, identification with a field of specialization, and the demand for engineers in various specializations. The relatively high stability rates for the civil, chemical, electrical, and mechanical engineers may be due to the fact that their curricula are so specialized and distinct that field switching is difficult. Also, these are the oldest specializations in engineering, with the strongest professional associations, and they encourage stressing "chemical" instead of "engineer," for example. Strong subfield identifications would certainly limit the emergence of a single profession whose members share a common designation.

Some of the diversity that characterizes engineering graduates can be seen here if the curriculum differences that are found in engineering schools in the United States are considered. If the engineering curriculum is divided into four main areas—mathematics and physical science; engineering science; engineering design, analysis, and systems; and humanities and social sciences—a wide range of emphasis on these areas is found in the undergraduate curriculum of engineers. One-half of the engineers report having had over 40 percent of their curriculum devoted to mathematics and physical sciences, whereas over one-third report having devoted less than 25 percent of their curriculum to such areas. A very similar dispersed distribution is found for the engineering science subjects and the engineering design subjects. The closest thing to a commonly shared subject matter emphasis is found with respect to the humanities and social sciences, where approximately two-thirds of the engineers report an undergraduate curriculum that devoted less than 20 percent to these areas.

Professional Socialization

Courses and curricula are only one aspect of the professional school's role in preparing its practitioners. Of equal importance is the school's role in transmitting values, establishing identifications, and encouraging commitments in matters that will aid the personal development of the student and lay the basis for his professional development. Because these matters are not handled through formal course instruction but through more or less informal associations, it is important that the professional school provide opportunities for the student to have contact with other students and with faculty. Student contact can lead to the emergence of a student subculture that encourages positive ties with engineering, and it can also provide a ready source of social support for coping with the many stress situations that arise in the educational experience. Faculty contact provides for professional role models that the student can use for developing a professional self-image and for learning some of the folklore of the profession.

In professional schools of law, medicine, and the clergy, close associations with other aspiring and established practitioners are accomplished by a fairly complete isolation of the students from other students and faculty not in their discipline. This isolation can more readily take place when there has been a pre-professional education with more general exposure to a variety of students, faculty, and subject matter. However, in engineering schools there is the double burden of providing a basic undergraduate education and providing professional training in a four-year program. To achieve both of these objectives is often quite difficult, and this tends to be one of the persistent dilemmas of engineering education. Yet, the engineering students' interest in other programs in the physical sciences, and particularly in business schools, and the continuing demand for engineering graduates in industry and government clearly indicate that undergraduate engineering must be doing its job rather well. Although this is probably true, the objectives of undergraduate engineering education are often achieved at the expense of the general education of the student and at the expense of his professional socialization. The primary factor involved here is the very heavy and demanding course loads that engineers are required to take and that limit his contact with students, faculty, and the larger university community.

One of the problems facing engineering educators has been to find the particular balance of courses needed to make engineering education a general education as well as a professional education. The movement toward a more broadly based undergraduate education that has taken place during the last several decades has often led to the addition of new courses in the curriculum without a corresponding "paring down" of outmoded courses. These new additions proceeded at such a pace that engineering hourly credit requirements have increased to the point where only with great difficulty can a student obtain the baccalaureate degree in four years. The data collected from a randomly selected sample of fifty-two colleges and universities indicate that, as compared to mathematics, physics, and chemistry requirements, engineering demands almost an additional semester's work for the degree. The mean semester hour requirement in engineering was 143.7, whereas the science and mathematics average was 129.6. The range in engineering went from a low of 120 hours to a high of 153 hours; in science and mathematics the low was 113 hours, and the high was 144 hours.

One way in which a demanding curriculum can affect students is to reduce academic performance in such a way as to obtain a faulty estimate of the abilities of students. James A. Davis' study of a national sample of college graduates reports that engineering students were very low on an academic performance index, which was based upon grades and quality of school.[21] It is difficult to reconcile this relatively low academic performance with the fact that engineering students are recruited in much higher proportions from the most talented high school graduates than students in any other undergraduate major.[22] A comparison of Davis' data on academic performance with the *Project Talent* data on measured aptitude of students choosing various college majors indicates that students in fields with measured aptitude lower than engineering students still obtained higher grades in college. One plausible explanation for this is that good grades are much more difficult to come by in engineering because of the difficulty of the total program or that grading procedures in engineering courses are more stringent. An interesting and important study would be to attempt to determine if the engineering student's apparent limited interest in graduate study may be due as much to low grades and the discouraging experience of a demanding program as to the lack of resources or interest.

The demanding nature of the engineering curriculum may also be responsible for the limited time that is available for students to become involved in the larger university community. A small group of freshmen engineers was asked to keep a detailed diary during four separate weeks in their first semester. The time devoted to studying outside of the classroom during the four weeks averaged thirty hours per week per student.[23] Because most of this time was recorded for evening and weekends, limited time was available for university functions such as films, lectures, concerts, or other leisure activities. Data from a larger sample of 300 freshman engineering students indicate that only approximately 10 percent of the engineering students were frequent attenders of these university functions and 10 percent or less were frequent attenders of college dances or movies in the community or frequent viewers of television. Attendance at football and basketball games was the most popular, with a little over 50 percent indicating frequent attendance.[24] Thus, engineering students probably tend to have a restricted experience at college in terms of both curriculum and the general social and cultural life on the campus.

Finally, some aspect of the character of the en-

gineering school, whether it be a demanding curriculum, poorly structured classroom situations, or the
size of the school, inhibits the development of student-
faculty contact and thereby impairs the communication of educational and professional values. One study
of the alumni at a large engineering school indicates
that some two-thirds or more of the alumni reported
that they had never had contact with their professors
outside of the classroom in such situations as coffee
breaks, lunch, visits to their homes, or informal con-
versations on social and political issues.[25] This was also
true for about one-half to one-third of the people working on their doctorate degree. Without such contact,
the student's ability to develop a professional self-
image is impaired due to the absence of available role
models.

One estimate of the extent to which professional
socialization may be impaired in professional schools
can be obtained by comparing the educational and
professional views of persons at various points in their
engineering careers. A study conducted at one large
engineering school reported the views of engineering
alumni, engineering faculty, engineering seniors, and
engineering freshmen on twenty-six general and specific objectives of a college education.[26] Several important patterns that may shed some light on the
effectiveness of professional socialization in engineering school may be observed from these data.

In terms of overall comparisons among the four
groups on the importance they attached to various
educational objectives, twenty-one of the twenty-six
contained statistically significant differences for the
four groups. In terms of differences in views between
various groups all possible paired groups can be ordered in terms of their agreement on the importance

of the educational objectives. The groups are in the following rank order going from high to low agreement:

	Average Discrepancy per Educational Objective
Alumni—seniors	6%
Alumni—faculty	7
Faculty—seniors	9
Seniors—freshmen	12
Alumni—freshmen	14
Faculty—freshmen	19

The rank order of agreement closely parallels the temporal and social distance that exists between the groups. The effect of adult socialization can also be observed from the fact that seniors have much higher agreement with faculty than do freshmen. However, the two groups most critical for transmitting professional values to freshmen—seniors and faculty—are still markedly dissimilar in their views from freshmen. If the items themselves and the pattern of differences are closely looked at, the points at which the socialization process is most and least effective may be discerned. Socialization is assumed to be most effective when the differences between faculty and seniors are smaller than the differences between faculty and freshmen and between seniors and freshmen. Socialization is least effective when the differences between faculty and seniors and between faculty and freshmen are greater than the differences between seniors and freshmen. This latter pattern may also be indicative of a strong oppositional student subculture that hampers socialization. The data indicate that lowest effectiveness in socialization was found on items dealing with developing social skills, attaining emotional and social adjustment, and developing a broad general outlook while becoming familiar with a variety of subjects. In each case, the seniors and freshmen were more likely to attribute importance to them.

The most effective socialization, in terms of seniors having greater agreement with faculty than freshmen, was on items dealing with developing the ability to do independent research, preparation for advanced study, and a general mastery of knowledge and skills leading to proficiency and expertness in one's field. However, the effect of the socialization experience, although it brings seniors and faculty into closer agreement, is to encourage advanced students to place less, rather than more, emphasis upon these educational objectives. The experiences that take place between the freshman year and the senior year may lead to a kind of cynical sophistication regarding educational matters. This experience may be analogous to the way in which the medical student transforms his images of medicine in the face of the harsh realities of real medical decisions.[27]

Knowledge, Power, and Social Responsibility

In this chapter the many divisive and segmenting factors in engineering education and those aspects of the structure and control of undergraduate curricula that hamper the development of a strong commitment to engineering as a profession have been discussed. Yet, more is involved than simply an academic interest in the struggle of various occupations to try to achieve professional status. As pointed out in Chapter 1, the professions in modern industrial societies play an important integrative role in dealing with a variety of crisis situations that individuals are unable to handle for themselves. The established professions have traditionally dealt with the problems of individuals and have been concerned with the problems of society only in the cumulative or aggregate sense. (There are, of course, established professionals who serve "society," such as public health physicians). Engineering, however, has been moving more and more in the direction of trying to solve large-scale societal problems with technological means. Such efforts directed at the design of complex technical-social systems will have far-reaching consequences for human values and the very fabric of society. These will be social responsibilities on a scale never before experienced by a single profession. For this reason, therefore, it may be vitally important for engineering students in the decades ahead to have a strong sense of social responsibility and service ethic to their society and for their education to be designed to prepare them to handle human values in their work.

The difficulties of educating a professional person with a wisdom and breadth of perspective necessary to go along with expert knowledge are shared by all professions. As Alfred North Whitehead has noted, professionalized knowledge "produces minds in a groove," and this is true for the physician, the engineer, and the lawyer.[28] Yet, that which distinguishes the engineer from other professions and raises the question of social responsibility and service to society to a position of central importance is that engineers in the future will wield an influence and power far greater than that ever enjoyed by other professional groups. The physician or lawyer who places self-interest above his service to clients is far less a social menace than the expert whose facility for technical solutions obscures his ability to consider human values. The difference between these situations may be best understood in terms of the social costs of errors by professionals.

Others have recognized the subtle, yet significant, difference between those who pursue knowledge as an end and those who pursue it with utilitarian motives. Bertrand Russell has written of the twofold impulse responsible for the growth of science: "We may seek knowledge of an object because we love the object or because we wish to have power over it. The former impulse leads to knowledge that is contemplative, the latter to the kind that is practical." [29]

Russell has also suggested that those who are guided by these impulses also adopt particular postures toward the world in which they live:

When science is considered contemplatively, not practically, we find that what we believe, we believe owing to animal faith, and it is only our disbeliefs that are due to science. When, on the other hand, science is considered as a technique for the transformation of ourselves and our environment, it is found to give us power quite independent of its metaphysical validity. But we can only wield this power by ceasing to ask ourselves metaphysical questions as to the nature of reality. Yet these questions are the evidence of a lover's attitude towards the world. *Thus it is only in so far as we renounce the world as its lovers that we can conquer it as its technicians.*[30]

Russell's comments are quite similar to Whitehead's concern over the education of professionals.

The dangers arising from this aspect of professionalism are great, particularly in our democratic societies. The directive force of reason is weakened. The leading intellects lack balance. They see this set of circumstances, or that set; but not both sets together. The task of coordination is left to those who lack either the force or the character to succeed in some definite career. In short, the specialized functions of the community are performed better and more progressively but the generalised direction lacks vision. The progressiveness in detail only adds to the danger produced by the feebleness of coordination.[31]

The concerns of both Russell and Whitehead take on added significance when the growing importance of engineering in a technological society is considered. As engineers become more involved in positions of power and influence, where the ends of their activity extend beyond technical matters, the quality of their educational experience takes on greater significance.

NOTES

1. C. R. Mann, *A Study of Engineering Education,* Bulletin 11 (The Carnegie Foundation for the Advancement of Teaching, 1918).
2. W. E. Wickenden, *Report of The Investigation of Engineering Education, 1923–1929* (Pittsburgh: Society for The Promotion of Engineering Education, 1930).
3. H. P. Hammond, "Engineering Education After the War," *Journal of Engineering Education,* 34 (May 1944), 589–614; L. E. Grinter, "A Manual on Graduate Study in Engineering," *Journal of Engineering Education,* 35 (June 1945), 615–652.
4. L. E. Grinter, "Report on Evaluation of Engineering Education," *Journal of Engineering Education,* 46 (September 1955), 25–63.
5. Robert William Perrucci, William K. LeBold, and Warren A. Howland, "The Engineer in Industry and

Government," *Journal of Engineering Education*, 57 (March 1966), 237–273, see esp. 242.

6. For a discussion of the problems of obsolescence among engineers, see T. Paul Torda (ed.), *Proceedings: Midwest Conference in Reducing Obsolescence of Engineering Skills* (Illinois Institute of Technology, March 1963).

7. Even the most vocal critics of narrow specialization in higher education have recognized this shift and have responded to it favorably. See, for example, Paul Goodman, *Compulsory Mis-Education and the Community of Scholars* (New York: Vintage, 1966), p. 123.

8. Select Committee on Government Research, *Manpower for Research and Development* (Washington D.C.: U.S. Government Printing Office, 1964).

9. Goals of Engineering Education Committee, *Preliminary Report, Goals of Engineering Education* (Lafayette, Ind.: Purdue University, American Society of Engineering Education, 1965).

10. See, for example, the entire issue, *Design*, 67 (March 31, 1966) and *Chemical Engineering Process* (February 1966).

11. William J. Goode, "Encroachment, Charlatinism, and the Emerging Profession: Psychology, Sociology, and Medicine," *American Sociological Review*, 25 (December 1960), 902–914.

12. National Science Foundation, *Scientists, Engineers and Technicians in the 1960's, Requirements and Supply*, paper NSF 83–84 (Washington, D.C.: National Science Foundation, 1964), pp. 34–36.

13. Phillip Patrick, "Tenth Annual Survey of Engineering-Technician Enrollment and Graduation," *Journal of Engineering Education*, 56 (September 1965), 14–15.

14. Jesse J. Defore, "Baccalaureate Programs in Engineering Technology: A Study of Their Emergence and of Some Characteristics of Their Content" (unpublished Ph.D. dissertation, Florida State University, 1966).

15. *Ibid.*, p. 159.

16. *Ibid.*, p. 161.

17. Harold L. Wilensky, "The Professionalization of Every-

one?" *American Journal of Sociology,* 70 (September 1964), p. 148.

18. William J. Goode, "Community Within a Community: The Professions," *American Sociological Review,* 22 (April 1957), 194–200.
19. M. Schwartz, *The U.S. College Educated Population* (Chicago: National Opinion Research Center), pp. 72–75.
20. Wilensky, *op. cit.,* p. 148.
21. James A. Davis, *Great Aspirations* (Chicago: Aldine, 1964).
22. John C. Flanagan *et al., Project Talent: The American High School Student,* Research Project No. 635 (Pittsburgh: University of Pittsburgh, Project Talent Office, 1964).
23. Richard W. Wunderlich, "Freshmen Engineers: A Study of Occupational Commitment" (unpublished M.S. thesis, Purdue University, 1966), pp. 54–55.
24. Graham C. Kinloch, "Commitment, Expectations and Experience: A Study of Engineering Freshmen" (unpublished M.S. thesis, Purdue University, 1966), pp. 45–49.
25. Carolyn Cummings Perrucci and William K. LeBold, "The Engineer and Scientist: Student, Professional and Citizen" (mimeo, Purdue University, 1967).
26. George A. Hawkins, Edward C. Thoma, and William K. LeBold, "A Study of the Purdue University Engineering Graduate," *Journal of Engineering Education,* 49 (June 1959), 930–947.
27. Howard S. Becker and Blanche Geer, "The Fate of Idealism in Medical School," *American Sociological Review,* 23 (February 1958), 50–56.
28. Alfred North Whitehead, *Science and the Modern World* (New York: Mentor, 1948), p. 196.
29. Bertrand Russell, "Science and Values," in Hans Kohn (ed.), *The Modern World: 1848 To The Present* (New York: Macmillan, 1963), p. 286.
30. *Ibid.,* p. 288.
31. Whitehead, *op. cit.,* p. 197.

4

BASES
OF
PROFESSIONALISM

The dual processes of selection and socialization have a major impact upon the character of the engineering profession. Students with particular interests, abilities, and values are selectively recruited into different fields of study. The interaction between the attributes of the students and the requirements of the professional schools serves to produce a set of experiences that leaves its mark upon the profession. The particular experiences in the professional schools begin to shape the novice in ways that also influence the emerging nature of the profession itself.

In the two preceding chapters considerable attention was devoted to the characteristics of engineering students and engineering education. The pattern that emerged from the information examined was that the engineering profession is characterized by considerable diversity in terms of both the students and the educational experiences provided by the professional schools. This diversity is due not only to the varied nature of students and schools in any particular historical period but also to the major educational differences that separate engineers of different generations.

The early professional socialization of the student engineer provides an important, but partial, set of influences upon the professional values and activities of the practicing engineer. If professionalization is viewed as a process, then the forces that influence a practicing engineer to behave in a more or less professional manner must be operative throughout his career. A student whose professional socialization has led him to subscribe to, and actively support, professional values might find such early commitments extinguished after a few years of working in an organization that pays little more than lip service to the professional interests and needs of its engineers.

A considerable body of literature has already been devoted to documenting the areas of conflict between organizations and professionals.[1] Organizations are usually described in terms of their needs for predictable behavior, coordination of activities, loyalty to the organization, and the use of economic criteria in selecting organizational goals. These needs are satisfied through such operational procedures as an emphasis upon bureaucratic rules, authority vested in established hierarchies, rewards based upon "local" orientations, and an emphasis upon utilitarian concerns in judging the merits of a professional's work.

Professionals, on the other hand, are said to emphasize authority based upon knowledge rather than hierarchical position, freedom from external control in matters related to their work, commitment to colleagues as the main source of professional rewards, and a strong service ethic or sense of social responsibility. William Kornhauser has pointed to the conflicts between organizations and professionals over determining the proportion of an organization's resources that should be devoted to basic research as compared to applied research and to the criteria that should be utilized (as well as who should establish the criteria) for hiring, firing, and promoting in the organization.[2] Additional tensions are generated over the manner in which professional work is organized (functional groups or project groups), the use of nonprofessional supervisors, and the restrictions on the scientific norm of open communication of ideas to other members of the professional community.

Most of the work on organizations and professionals has been devoted to documenting the areas of conflict and accommodation between the two. This particular emphasis has led to a neglect of the important variations within organizations concerning their degree of bureaucratization and variations between professions and within the same profession. Some notable exceptions are found in the work of Richard H. Hall, which is concerned with variations in the bureaucratic model,[3] and the work of Harold L. Wilensky, which concerns differences among professions in the extent to which they follow a specific temporal sequence in such structural characteristics as university-based education, professional associations, and licensing laws.[4] Similarly, in the earlier chapters it was pointed out that the engineering profession was not composed of a homogeneous collection of practitioners dedicated to the same professional values, motivated by the same noble goals, and sharing the same educational and work experiences.

The effects that different educational backgrounds and work careers have upon the extent to which engineers subscribe to selected professional values and engage in selected professional activities are examined in this chapter. In this connection, the effects of such career characteristics as education, administrative functions, and level of technical and supervisory responsibility upon professional activities and values will be discussed.

The use of the term "profession" for a particular occupation or the term "professional" for the practitioners of that occupation usually implies a complex set of structural characteristics for the profession,[5] and an equally complex set of values, orientations, and behaviors for the practitioners.[6] In discussing professionals in this chapter, rather than professions, a wide variety of characteristics that have been attributed to professionals will be referred to. These characteristics include professional values or attitudes, such as the importance of autonomy in one's work; contact with colleagues at work; involvement in professional societies; the utilization of, and contribution to, the knowledge upon which the profession is based; and the importance of money, status, and prestige (this last value is viewed as nonprofessional in nature). Other characteristics consist of the professionals' reference groups or basic orientations, which is a way of determining if the professional is mainly concerned with his standing among his colleagues or if he would prefer the rewards and recognition of a group other than his professional community. This characteristic is usually associated with a view of the profession as a terminal career and not as a stepping stone to another occupation. The final set of characteristics fall into the same areas as those described above except that they are *behavioral* characteristics rather than attitudinal.

The literature includes some treatments of these professional values, activities, and orientations that point both to their relevance and to their lack of specificity. The autonomy variable has its roots in the relationship between the free professional and the "ignorant" client. As the holder of the expertise, the professional is expected to exercise his judgment free from the control of parties outside the relationship as well as free from the influence of the client. This latter aspect can be traced to Talcott Parsons' discussion of the role of effective neutrality in protecting the professional from the inner conflict that emotional involvement with a client can bring and for protecting the client from possible exploitation by the professional.[7] Autonomy, however, is never absolute; it is circumscribed both by the laws of the community and by the influence and knowledge of the client.

The autonomy dimension has taken on greater importance as professionals have moved into organizational settings in increasing numbers. Kornhauser's account of the concerns of scientists and engineers in industry over hiring, firing, and promoting colleagues, setting project goals, and evaluating performance points to the importance of autonomy for professionals. Yet, care must be taken to recognize the variability of work settings, work activities, and clients that can change the centrality of autonomy for professional performance. Mary E. Goss' paper on influence and authority among physicians clearly indicates that physicians in a hospital setting seem perfectly willing to give up some of their prerogatives, whereas at the same time they are very sensitive to encroachments in other areas.[8] Similarly, Gerald H. Moeller and W. W. Charters did not find bureaucratization in schools to be associated with an increased sense of powerlessness among teachers.[9] Kornhauser's findings, however, are for scientists and engineers in research and development laboratories, and these persons represent only a small fraction of all the science-based professionals in industry. Moreover, William M. Evan has suggested that conflict and role strain among scientific professionals is more likely to occur in applied, rather than basic, research settings.[10]

Therefore, the importance of autonomy for professionals may not be related simply to the opposing norms of professions and organizations. The existence of a client, the degree of similarity between the organization's goals and the professional's goals, and the particular professional prerogatives that the organization seeks to regulate may all influence the degree of conflict over the norm of autonomy.

The professional's sense of identification with his work and with a collectivity of other practitioners is held to be the basis for the importance of colleague contact and colleague rewards for acceptable and outstanding performance. This tie between self-image and collectivity has its origins in the periods of deliberate socialization where the neophyte is presented with new role models and new standards of worth. The process and pattern of identification has been documented and discussed by Robert K. Merton, Howard S. Becker, William J. Goode, Donald C. Lortie, James Carper, and others.[11]

As a consequence of this early and intensive socialization, many analysts have posited the existence of conflicting reference systems and loyalties for professionals in organizations. The earliest systematic conceptionalization of these reference systems in organizations was set forth by Alvin W. Gouldner in his use of Merton's distinction between "cosmopolitans" and "locals." [12] Gouldner said:

[The cosmopolitan is] low on loyalty to the employing organization, high on commitment to specialized role skills, and likely to use an outer [professional] reference group orientation.

[The local is] high on loyalty to the employing organization, low on commitment to specialized role skills, and likely to use an inner [organizational] reference group orientation.[13]

The cosmopolitan, because of his collegial reference system, is more likely to engage in publishing, because this is a major means by which he achieves the rewards that collegial bodies can bestow. This expectation has been confirmed in research on scientific productivity among scientists and engineers.[14] Kornhauser recognized these two orientations as posing a basic dilemma for organizations who seek to obtain a close integration of their professionals into the organization and thereby suffer a loss of their professional worth.[15]

Although positing the existence of such conflicting orientations is conceptually neat, there is only very mixed evidence that they are empirically exhaustive or exclusive. Wilensky developed indexes of a "professional-discipline orientation" and a "careerist orientation" that reflect the reference group concepts. His findings are:

As expected, the two indexes are negatively correlated
($r = -.27$, $p < .01$). Men who score very high on professionalism seldom score high on careerism; men who rate
very high on careerism seldom rate high on professionalism.
Taking account of the entire range, however, this inverse
relationship is not strong, which suggests that mixed types
of orientation are typical, consistent with the idea of the
interpenetration of bureaucratic and professional cultures.[16]

Barney G. Glaser's indexes of cosmopolitan and local
produced quite different results with over one-half
of his respondents classified as high on both indexes
($r = .70$).[17] He suggests that the alternative orientations are not necessarily inconsistent when the goals of
organizations and professionals are congruent. This is
similar to Wilensky's view that many types of organizations may not be a barrier to professional commitment but may, in fact, encourage them.[18] Finally, in
this same connection, Simon Marcson found in the
organization he studied that professional success was
rewarded with organizational symbols of prestige and
income.[19]

All this suggests, of course, that the clarity of different career orientations and their consequences may
be very dependent upon the exact settings in which
professionals are employed. The nature of the rewards
offered by professional and organizational bodies is
also of importance because an orientation, whether
cosmopolitan, local, or any other, will not be sustained
without positive reinforcement. These points may be
especially true for engineers where the distinction
between professional interests and organizational interests is very unclear. In using a modification of

Wilensky's professional and careerist orientations for a sample of about 3000 engineers, a positive correlation of .45 for the two indexes was found. The use of such orientations as cosmopolitan and local would therefore seem to be of greater value if examined in connection with different organizational and career patterns.

It is important to note that in this chapter the main concern is the examination of the characteristics of professionals in their most elementary form. For example, in each of the professional value areas a number of individual items that are believed to measure the value will be used, at the same time avoiding any effort to combine the individual items into composite measures. In so doing two very important questions concerning the dimensions or characteristics of professionals will also be avoided. The first question is whether or not the larger number of characteristics of professionals can be reduced to several manageable dimensions or, if not, which characteristics of professionals seem to be most highly associated. The second question concerns the degree of correspondence between attitudinal measures of professionals and behavioral measures. Are professionals who are most likely to subscribe to the values of autonomy, contribution to knowledge, colleague control, and so on, the same ones whose behavior most closely measures up to the value preferences? The differences between the word and the deed may provide an important basis for examining variations within the same profession, between professionals in different types of organizations, or among different types of professionals. This question, however, has received relatively little attention from those concerned with the study of the professions.

Professional Values

In examining professional values six value areas are
considered that are generally used to distinguish
professionals from nonprofessionals. They are: (1)
challenging nature of work, (2) pecuniary and career
rewards, (3) autonomy in one's work, (4) association
with colleagues, (5) involvement in a professional
community, and (6) contributions to knowledge and
society. Table 4–1 shows the percentages of engineers
answering "very important to me personally" for items
in each of the six value areas; these percentages are
presented for engineers of different degree levels.
Several things can be determined from the percentages
in Table 4–1: the degree of importance that engineers
attach to the different value areas and the differences
that exist between graduate degree engineers and
nongraduate degree engineers.

The value areas in Table 4–1 reveal several patterns. First there is the variability of the distributions
produced by items grouped in the same value area.
For example, in the autonomy area, two items produce
60 percent responses of very important, while two
items produce about 20 percent saying very important.
In some cases this may be due to the social desirabil-
ity of the item (for example, "to enhance status and
prestige" in the advancement value area may not be
the popular thing to say) or that the item may simply
not belong in that value cluster because it is probably
measuring something else. The second notable feature
of Table 4–1 is that the value areas can be roughly
ordered in terms of their importance to engineers.
The challenge value seems to be clearly most important
to engineers, reflecting the intrinsic appeal of their

work. Advancement and autonomy values are second and third, with little real difference between the two. Colleague values rank fourth in importance and professional community values and knowledge values rank a distant fifth and sixth. The curious pattern of the items in the professional community value area is worth noting, with almost one-half of the engineers endorsing the importance of being treated as a professional by superiors but very few subscribing to those things that would seem to enhance professional status (for example, belonging to a professional community outside work, time for outside professional society work, and belonging to an organization highly regarded by the profession).

One of the clearer patterns that emerges from Table 4–1 is that engineers with the doctorate degree are distinguished from their colleagues without the doctorate in the importance they attach to specific value areas. Engineers with doctorate degrees give greater importance to having contact with colleagues, to belonging to a professional community, to contributing to knowledge, and to the challenges that are intrinsic in engineering work. They give less importance to pecuniary rewards and career advancement than do engineers without the doctorate degree. There were no degree differences among engineers in the importance they attach to maintaining autonomy over their own work.

The fact that degree differences exist in each of the value areas other than autonomy suggests that the importance of freedom and autonomy for the engineer may be more closely associated with work settings and organization settings than with the socialization of advanced degree education. It may also suggest that autonomy in organizations is important only for those

TABLE 4-1   *Professional Values by Degree Level**

Opportunities	Degree			All Respondents
	B.S.	M.S.	Ph.D.	
Challenge				
To innovate	72%	77%	83%	74%
For challenging work	82	90	94	85
For problems lacking ready-made solutions	58	64	79	61
To see ideas put to use	71	71	62	70
Advancement				
To advance economically	61	54	46	58
To enhance status and prestige	13	14	11	13
For career line of increasing rewards and promotions	35	33	23	33
To advance in my position	63	62	48	62
To move into management	43	41	27	41
Autonomy				
To be free of supervision	22	21	29	22
To make most decisions connected with my work	60	60	60	60
For freedom to manage my work	62	62	69	62
To fix my own work schedule	21	20	24	22
Colleagues				
To associate with engineers and scientists	31	38	51	35
To discuss my ideas with colleagues	43	45	56	45
To have respect of colleagues because of technical achievement	39	46	53	42
To work with colleagues interested in latest developments	42	49	61	46

TABLE 4–1 *Professional Values by Degree Level** *(Continued)*

	Degree			All Respond- ents
Opportunities	B.S.	M.S.	Ph.D.	
Professional Community				
To belong to a professional community outside of work	9	13	20	11
To be treated as professional by superiors	44	50	52	46
To belong to an organization highly regarded by my profession	17	25	26	19
For outside professional society work	5	6	10	6
Knowledge				
To publish	8	19	49	15
To contribute to basic scientific knowledge	11	19	40	16
To contribute to society	24	25	35	26

* Percent responding "very important".

professions that have their historical roots in independent practice, which makes them more sensitive to the organizational setting. Engineering, on the other hand, can be viewed as a profession that emerged within an organizational context and therefore does not have the professional values that would make autonomy and freedom an issue in one's work. A similar response can be expected from physicians and lawyers as organizational employment becomes more prevalent and if they are prepared for such employment in their professional education.

The importance of the doctorate degree is further established by the difference between the degree holders. Engineers with the master's degree are much closer to their colleagues with the bachelor's degree than those with the doctorate degree. Apparently, a combination of the selection process and the extended period of professional socialization for the doctorate serves to produce engineers who are more inclined to support selected professional values.

The importance that these professional values have for engineers may also be influenced by certain aspects of an engineering career. In Table 4–2 the percentages subscribing to each value for three career dimensions are given. The career dimensions are: (1) the particular balance between technical and administrative activities in one's work, (2) the degree of technical responsibility of an engineer in terms of the extent of expert knowledge required for the position, and (3) the degree of supervisory responsibility of an engineer in terms of the level of personnel he supervises.

The specific job descriptions used for the career levels in Tables 4–2, 4–4, and 4–6 are listed below.

TECHNICAL-ADMINISTRATIVE FUNCTION

1. Entirely technical

2. Primarily technical

3. Half technical, half administrative

4. Primarily administrative, technical background necessary

5. Primarily administrative, technical background not necessary

6. Entirely administrative, technical background necessary

7. Entirely administrative, technical background not necessary

SUPERVISORY RESPONSIBILITY

1. No supervisory responsibility
2. Supervision of nontechnical personnel
3. Supervision of technical personnel only (except engineering and scientific)
4. Supervision of technical and nontechnical personnel (except engineering and scientific)
5. Supervision of professional engineering and scientific personnel
6. Supervision of lower management personnel
7. Supervision of middle management personnel
8. Responsible only to highest administrative offices
9. Hold highest administrative position

TECHNICAL RESPONSIBILITY

1. Simple operations following prescribed procedures. Judgment and knowledge based on previous experience are not required.

2. Responsibility for carrying out a sequence of standardized or prescribed operations.

3. Specific tasks oriented toward the practical application of theory and basic principles. Performs calculations applying standard formulas.

4. Using prescribed methods, performs work on specific and somewhat limited work assignments. Make tentative and preliminary selections and adaptations of alternatives.

5. Devises and recommends alternative methods of standardized analysis as a basis for solving problems. Only infrequently do assignments require the solution of difficult or unusual problems.

6. Performs a variety of assignments in which complex features occur on a regular and recurring basis. Improve, extend, or validate currently known precedents, data, methods, or techniques rather than to develop completely new ones.

7. Plans and conducts work requiring pioneering in areas in which large blocks of data are controversial or completely unknown. Proposals for new or additional work are usually recognized and accepted as those of an authority.

8. Conceives, plans and conducts pioneering work of outstanding scope and complexity in unexplored or heretofore unpromising areas. Serves as a nationally recognized authority in a specialized field.

First, considering the effect of the technical-administrative balance upon professional values, notable differences are found in those value areas designated as "advancement," "colleagues," "knowledge," and "professional community." Engineers whose positions are primarily administrative (levels 4 through 7) are more likely to subscribe to values concerned with economic and career advancement than are those engineers whose positions are entirely technical (level 1). On the other hand, engineers who are in entirely technical positions are more likely to stress the importance of having contact with colleagues concerning their work. Engineers without administrative duties are also more likely to subscribe to publishing and contributing to basic scientific knowledge as important professional values. With respect to the "professional community" values, pronounced differences are found between administrative and nonadministrative engineers, with some tendency for the latter to put more emphasis upon being treated as a professional. No discernible pattern of differences was found for the "autonomy" and "challenge" values.

The extent of technical responsibility embodied in an engineer's position also seems to affect his reaction to professional values. Engineers whose work is in pioneering areas and who might be considered as authorities in their field (levels 7 and 8) are most different from their colleagues in the value clusters of "challenge," "autonomy," "colleagues," "professional community," and "knowledge." The general pattern that may be seen in Table 4–2 concerning technical responsibility is that as the level of knowledge and expertise of an engineer increases so does the likelihood that he will subscribe to certain professional values. (What is obtained from this finding and other findings on the effect of responsibility is, of course, the combined effect of the doctorate degree *and* holding positions of high technical responsibility. However, because doctorate degree engineers comprise only about one-fourth of all the engineers in high technical responsibility positions, apparently the career factors do make an independent contribution to professional values and activities.)

The final aspect of the career that may influence an engineer's response to professional values is the level of supervisory responsibility associated with his position. Whereas the level of technical responsibility was concerned with the degree of expertise of an engineer, level of supervisory responsibility is concerned with authority. Authority appears to be directly associated with professional values only in the areas of "challenge" and "autonomy." In both these areas, however, the degree of association does not seem to be as pronounced as it was with respect to technical responsibility.

TABLE 4-2 Professional Values by Selected Career Patterns*

Opportunities	Technical-Administrative Function				Technical Responsibility			Supervisory Responsibility		
	1	2	3	4-7	1-5	6	7-8	1	2-4	5-9
Challenge										
To innovate	74.2%	74.7%	74.3%	73.6%	61.4%	72.4%	85.8%	69.4%	75.0%	77.1%
For challenging work	86.0	85.8	83.9	82.2	74.2	84.7	91.5	83.4	83.6	86.1
For problems lacking ready-made solutions	65.7	60.9	58.5	62.2	74.6	58.4	75.2	57.3	58.8	65.8
To see ideas put to use	66.1	71.3	71.1	70.4	66.6	70.2	73.0	63.0	73.0	70.3
Advancement										
To advance economically	50.4	57.5	61.7	59.7	58.2	58.4	56.4	57.3	62.1	55.7
To enhance status and prestige	12.9	11.4	14.0	12.8	16.1	11.9	10.6	13.1	14.2	11.2
For career line of increasing rewards and promotions	31.6	30.3	36.7	34.5	33.5	34.1	30.9	34.9	35.0	30.9
To advance in my position	55.7	60.0	64.5	65.3	63.9	62.0	59.2	61.8	64.3	60.0
To move into management	21.4	30.8	46.0	64.5	40.4	39.9	41.9	33.3	40.6	46.4

Autonomy										
To be free of supervision	25.9	19.8	23.3	22.8	16.1	22.6	26.3	20.7	21.7	24.1
To make most decisions connected with my work	59.8	56.0	63.5	65.3	53.5	59.2	68.2	55.5	60.6	64.5
For freedom to manage my work	59.5	57.2	67.1	68.3	54.5	59.9	72.2	56.6	61.4	67.9
To fix my own work schedule	24.7	22.1	21.1	19.1	22.3	20.6	22.6	21.1	23.5	20.9
Colleagues										
To associate with engineers and scientists	47.4	37.0	33.8	25.5	27.1	32.9	44.9	37.5	32.4	35.5
To discuss my ideas with colleagues	56.7	44.7	42.2	40.1	40.7	43.0	51.0	46.7	44.0	44.2
To have respect of colleagues because of technical achievement	49.1	43.8	42.4	35.1	34.7	41.5	49.0	41.7	41.4	43.3
To work with colleagues interested in latest developments	54.9	46.2	43.7	41.6	37.5	42.2	57.6	44.9	43.4	48.1
Professional Community										
To belong to a professional community outside of work	13.1	11.2	10.5	11.4	8.1	10.3	15.4	11.0	10.2	12.2

109

TABLE 4-2 *Professional Values by Selected Career Patterns* (Continued)

Opportunities	Technical-Administrative Function				Technical Responsibility			Supervisory Responsibility		
	1	2	3	4–7	1–5	6	7–8	1	2–4	5–9
To be treated as professional by superiors	49.4	48.3	43.9	39.9	39.5	46.2	51.4	43.8	47.3	47.5
To belong to an organization highly regarded by my profession	22.5	18.1	19.2	19.1	14.8	17.5	25.8	14.0	19.2	21.1
For outside professional society work	7.1	6.3	6.2	5.8	5.0	5.5	8.6	5.5	6.0	7.1
Knowledge										
To publish	25.7	17.4	11.3	7.3	7.8	11.5	25.3	16.2	12.5	15.4
To contribute to basic scientific knowledge	29.2	17.3	12.8	7.1	9.9	12.2	25.6	18.3	12.6	16.0
To contribute to society	28.8	25.1	25.6	24.3	23.7	24.4	29.0	23.6	25.8	27.0

* Percent responding "very important."

In general, the professional values examined seem to be most closely associated with an engineer's level of education, the extent of expertise and knowledge manifested in his work, and the extent of his involvement in administrative activities in his work. Advanced degree engineers are more likely to underscore the importance of professional values than are engineers in positions with considerable technical responsibility. Involvement in administrative activities, on the other hand, shows little difference for the challenge, advancement, and autonomy values, but it is indirectly associated with the colleagues, professional community, and knowledge values. Supervisory responsibility is only moderately associated with the professional values examined in the section.

Professional Activities

Although the values espoused by members of various occupational groups may be important clues to professionalism, the activities of these persons are of equal importance. Table 4–3 lists activities that engineers may have engaged in during the past year. These activities refer to exposure to knowledge through reading, exposure to colleagues through professional meetings, and the production of new knowledge through work on papers and patents. Differences in these activities are again compared for engineers of different degree levels.

The activities in Table 4–3 are roughly arranged to reflect an increasing degree of involvement in professional activities as you read from the top of the list to the bottom. Reading about new developments or discussing them with colleagues are more modest professional activities than are presenting technical papers

TABLE 4–3   *Professional Activities Engaged in During Previous Year by Degree Level*

Activity	Degree		
	B.S.	M.S.	Ph.D.
Read about new developments in newspapers and magazines	96%	97%	96%
Discussed new developments with associates	88	90	94
Subscribed to engineering or scientific periodicals	77	87	90
Read new technical books	50	61	85
Attended local technical meetings	55	60	74
Purchased new technical books	37	50	65
Wrote technical papers	13	26	62
Presented technical papers	7	13	36
Applied for, or was granted, patents	11	17	24

or applying for patents. The data show a clear correspondence between the extent of involvement implied by an activity and the magnitude of the degree differences in participating in the activity. Engineers with the doctorate degree are much more likely to have engaged in a professional activity than their non-doctorate colleagues, especially for those activities that represent more rather than less involvement (this pattern is not perfectly linear, however, because the magnitude of the degree differences does decline for the two most extreme involvement activities).

The degree differences on professional activities is often more pronounced than that found for the professional values (see Table 4–1). This is especially true for the distinctions between engineers with the master's degree and engineers with the bachelor's degree. These two groups are quite similar on the value items but dissimilar on the more critical activity items. Although the differences are not extremely pronounced, they are enough to suggest that some of the inducements for involvement in selected professional activities are not necessarily dependent upon the professional socialization process associated with the doctorate degree in engineering. The doctorate, on the other hand, does seem to account for the important differences among engineers on professional values. In addition, the extent of participation in professional activities among master's degree engineers is generally about midway between the bachelor's degree engineers and doctor's degree engineers.

Considering the effects of different career lines upon professional activities, Table 4–4 shows, first of all, that involvement in administrative activities is not directly related to engaging in professional activities. At the more modest levels of activity (reading and discussing new developments and subscribing to journals), there is no relationship according to the technical-administrative balance. Involvement in the more advanced activities is much more likely to be found among engineers with no administrative duties than those with such duties. These findings are most pronounced for such activities as purchasing and reading new technical books and writing technical papers.

The level of technical responsibility of an engineer's position shows a very clear, direct relationship with involvement in professional activities. This direct relationship holds for each of the activities listed in Table 4–4. The effect of an increase in technical responsibility is most pronounced as the activity itself increases in the nature of the involvement implied by the activity. Thus, the differences between engineers

TABLE 4-4 *Professional Activities Engaged in During Previous Year by Selected Career Patterns*

Activity	Technical-Administrative Function				Technical Responsibility			Supervisory Responsibility		
	1	2	3	4-7	1-5	6	7-8	1	2-4	5-9
Read about new developments in newspapers and magazines	94.6%	96.8%	97.9%	95.6%	92.7%	97.1%	98.3%	96.1%	96.8%	96.8%
Discussed new developments with associates	86.9	90.6	91.3	83.9	77.3	89.9	94.9	85.5	87.2	91.7
Subscribed to engineering or scientific periodicals	78.3	78.3	88.3	79.6	70.4	78.2	89.9	74.5	77.6	85.6
Read new technical books	60.3	58.5	57.9	45.5	41.8	52.7	70.7	54.2	52.5	59.2
Attended local technical meetings	50.4	58.0	60.7	58.6	43.7	58.3	67.1	48.7	55.9	65.1
Attended national technical meetings	34.9	36.0	38.3	36.8	19.6	32.5	55.6	27.2	30.0	47.6
Purchased new technical books	54.8	42.3	44.6	31.9	34.6	39.0	54.0	42.3	37.4	46.2
Wrote technical papers	28.8	21.4	18.7	13.9	7.7	15.6	36.3	17.5	16.8	24.2
Presented technical papers	13.5	10.5	11.0	11.1	3.9	7.9	21.2	7.1	8.5	15.4
Applied for, or was granted, patents	15.5	17.1	14.0	46.5	4.9	11.0	25.1	9.2	14.5	16.8

who are high and low on expertise are small for such professional activities as reading and discussing new developments but become greater as the activity shifts to attending meetings, writing papers, and reading papers.

The degree of authority associated with an engineer's position is also directly associated with professional activities. But, unlike expertise, it is associated only with certain activities, and even with these in a more moderate fashion. Engineers at the highest authority levels are more likely to attend both local and national meetings, to write and present technical papers, and to apply for, or be granted, patents.

Thus, involvement in professional activities is most directly associated with level of education and with the extent of expertise associated with an engineer's position. Supervisory responsibility is also directly associated with many of the professional activities, but not as extensively as was found for education and expertise. Increased administrative activity was found to be directly associated with only a few of the professional activities.

A comparison of the findings concerning the relationship between professional values and professional activities reveals a similar pattern of findings with respect to the effects of education and technical responsibility. However, concerning involvement in administrative work and the level of supervisory responsibility of an engineer, the same pattern of findings with respect to both values and activities is not found. Supervisory responsibility has only a moderately direct association with professional values but a most substantially direct relationship with activities. Increased administrative involvement is found to be indirectly associated with professional values but it is directly

associated with some professional activities and indirectly associated with others. This may suggest that
whether or not an engineer engages in certain professional activities is often a function of his position, in
that such activities as attendance at meetings, subscribing to journals, presenting papers, and applying
for patents may be part of his job definition in those
positions of high authority and extensive administrative involvement. Apparently, involvement in such
activities need not be supported by a corresponding
preference for professional values. Thus, engineers in
high authority positions may attend meetings without
attributing much importance to colleague contact as
a professional value.

Professional Orientations

An important dimension of professionalism is the
extent to which each practitioner is oriented toward
his colleagues as the primary source of evaluation for
his own performance. This dimension is based upon
the observation that professionals obtain their major
rewards from their colleagues in the form of prestige
and deference. Such an orientation toward colleagues
often results in the profession itself establishing the
criteria for evaluating professional performance and
a resistance to control over performance by clients or
superiors in organizations.

Table 4–5 indicates the responses of engineers to a
question that asked them to rank the importance of
five different groups in evaluating the professional
performance of engineers. Existing theory concerning
the professions would suggest that the category of
"fellow engineers" should be selected as the most important group in the evaluation of performance. The

TABLE 4-5 *Professional Orientation by Degree Level*

Whose judgment should count in evaluating professional performance of engineers?	Degree		
	B.S.	M.S.	Ph.D.
Fellow engineers			
1. most important	23%	29%	36%
2.	44	46	44
3.	25	20	18
4.	5	4	1
5. least important	2	1	1
Immediate superiors in organization			
1. most important	55	54	45
2.	32	34	37
3.	10	9	10
4.	2	2	3
5. least important	1	1	1
Community leaders			
1. most important	1	1	*
2.	1	1	1
3.	4	2	2
4.	15	12	12
5. least important	79	84	84
Leaders of professional societies			
1. most important	4	4	4
2.	6	4	7
3.	27	33	40
4.	52	51	43
5. least important	11	8	5
Consumer of the product			
1. most important	18	14	11
2.	16	13	10
3.	33	35	29
4.	26	31	40
5. least important	7	7	9

* Indicates less than one percent.

data, however, show that "immediate superiors" are most frequently ranked as first in importance, followed by "fellow engineers," "consumers," "leaders of professional societies," and "community leaders." Although this pattern is found to hold for engineers at all degree levels, there is a tendency for larger proportions of advanced degree holders (especially holders of the Ph.D.) to rank "fellow engineers" first in importance.

Table 4-6 contains the orientation items for engineers in different managerial and technical careers. The main finding in Table 4-6 is that regardless of the extent of administrative duties, level of technical responsibility, and level of supervisory responsibility, engineers are most likely to select "immediate superiors" as the group whose judgment should count most in evaluating the professional performance of engineers. In this respect the findings are very similar to those obtained from the responses of engineers of different educational levels (see Table 4-5). The only career dimension that seems to have an effect upon professional orientation is the extent of administrative duties. Engineers with little or no administrative duties give more importance to "fellow engineers" in their professional orientation. In addition, the greater the amount of administrative duties of the engineer, the more importance he attributes to the "consumer of the product" for evaluating the performance of engineers.

These findings, in combination with the earlier findings on the importance of "autonomy" as a professional value, would suggest that some degree of incompatibility between professional and organizational norms dealing with autonomy may exist, but that it may not be problematic for engineers. Engineers' attitudes toward autonomy were found to involve the incorporation of this professional value as part of an occupational ideology—the majority feeling it important to have an opportunity to make decisions connected with their own work and to have freedom to manage their own work. At the same time, reflecting the facts of their occupational work-life, few engineers, especially those with a B.S. degree, feel that it is important to be free of supervision. The presence of organizational norms on autonomy is reflected in the fact that the engineers select their immediate superiors as most important in judging their professional performance.

The absence of any real conflict between organizational and professional norms concerning autonomy is suggested by the fact that the most professional engineers, as measured by the value, behavioral, and orientation items—the Ph.D. degree engineers and those in positions of high technical responsibility—do not respond any differently to the autonomy values than their less professional colleagues. This may reflect the changing conditions associated with the employment of professionals in large-scale organizations.

Organizational Policies on Professional Behavior

The final basis of support for professionalism can be found within the context of the organizations in which engineers are employed. The particuliar "climate" of an organization can encourage or discourage involvement in professional activities and in expressions of opinion concerning the prerequisites of a professional employee. One index to an organization's climate in this connection is its policies on encouraging and rewarding certain professionally relevant activities.

Table 4–7 indicates the responses of personnel men

TABLE 4-6 *Professional Orientation by Selected Career Patterns*

Whose judgment should count in evaluating professional performance of engineers?	Technical-Administrative Function				Technical Responsibility			Supervisory Responsibility		
	1	2	3	4–7	1–5	6	7–8	1	2–4	5–9
Fellow engineers										
1. most important	30.9%	29.4%	22.0%	19.8%	26.2%	25.1%	26.1%	29.2%	24.8%	23.4%
2.	47.3	45.2	45.3	42.0	42.1	45.9	45.3	44.0	46.0	44.8
3.	16.2	21.1	26.0	29.7	23.5	23.1	23.9	20.7	22.9	25.9
4.	4.4	3.2	4.2	5.9	6.1	4.2	3.0	4.4	4.6	4.1
5. least important	1.2	1.1	2.5	2.5	2.1	1.7	1.8	1.8	1.8	1.8
Immediate superiors in organization										
1. most important	55.8	51.9	55.6	56.7	52.0	55.6	54.7	52.3	54.8	56.2
2.	31.9	35.9	31.7	29.7	35.2	31.9	31.7	35.5	33.2	30.0
3.	9.6	10.0	10.1	10.4	9.8	9.6	11.1	9.4	8.7	11.3
4.	2.1	1.8	2.1	3.1	2.6	2.3	1.8	1.9	2.9	2.0
5. least important	.6	.3	.5	1.2	.5	.6	.7	.9	.4	.5

Community leaders										
1. most important	.9	.6	.4	.7	.6	.6	.7	.8	.5	.6
2.	1.1	.5	1.0	2.2	.6	1.4	1.0	1.2	.6	1.4
3.	3.0	2.8	3.1	5.1	3.7	3.8	2.7	3.4	3.7	3.3
4.	10.6	14.6	14.6	15.7	16.2	14.7	12.3	13.5	14.5	14.4
5. least important	84.5	81.6	80.9	76.2	78.8	79.6	83.3	81.0	80.7	80.4
Leaders of professional societies										
1. most important	4.2	3.6	4.0	3.1	5.3	3.0	3.7	4.5	3.5	3.2
2.	6.3	4.6	7.3	7.6	6.1	6.2	6.4	5.5	5.3	7.5
3.	38.1	31.4	26.9	24.3	29.1	29.4	30.4	30.4	30.6	28.6
4.	45.5	51.1	52.4	51.2	46.6	51.2	52.2	50.6	50.9	50.3
5. least important	5.9	9.3	9.4	13.8	12.8	10.2	7.2	8.9	9.7	10.4
Consumer of the product										
1. most important	9.7	15.0	19.3	20.3	17.0	16.8	15.7	14.5	17.1	17.9
2.	12.5	13.6	13.9	21.6	15.4	14.3	14.8	13.3	14.6	15.6
3.	33.0	34.5	33.5	29.3	33.5	33.7	31.9	35.5	33.9	30.9
4.	37.0	28.9	36.3	22.7	28.0	27.3	30.4	39.3	27.0	28.8
5. least important	7.8	7.9	6.6	6.2	6.0	7.9	7.2	7.4	7.5	6.9

and engineers to a question that asked whether or not their organization has a policy of encouraging and rewarding certain activities. In addition to the fact that engineers and personnel representatives do not show a high degree of agreement on the nature of organizational policies, at least one-half of the organizations (in the person of the personnel representative) neither encourage nor reward the listed activities. Educational activities are most likely to be encouraged and rewarded, followed by belonging to, and participating in, professional society activities. Publishing was also low among the listed activities, with encouragement for the pursuit of personal projects almost nonexistent.

TABLE 4–7 *Personnel Representatives' and Engineers' Views on Activities Encouraged and Rewarded by Organizations*

Activity	"Encourages Much"		"Rewards Much"	
	Per- sonnel	Engi- neers	Per- sonnel	Engi- neers
Advanced degree work	42%	23%	44%	24%
Refresher courses	41	20	25	12
Belonging to professional societies	39	20	12	5
Papers at professional engineering meetings	36	15	10	6
Attendance at professional engineering meetings	35	16	19	4
Becoming a registered professional engineer	31	17	14	7
Publication in professional engineering journals	27	14	11	7
Pursuing "pet" projects on company time	2	1	2	1

In light of the data that were examined earlier in this chapter, the encouragement of advanced degree work would be the activity most related to professionalism. If this activity is singled out for closer examination, a better picture of the extent to which professionalism is encouraged (either consciously or inadvertently) by organizations may be obtained. Figure 4–1 shows the breakdown of the extent of encouragement and reward of advanced degree work for organizations in the different industries in which engineers are employed. The relationship between type of industry and encouragement for advanced degree work is clear, with about three-fourths of research and development and aerospace organizations encouraging the policy and none of the construction firms doing so.

This pattern of support by organizations for advanced degree work indicates considerable industry-wide variation. The support that does exist is distributed in such a fashion as to lead to greater segmentation among engineers. Because there often tends to be an industry-wide basis for many professional and technical societies in engineering, great diversity of views represented at professional forums concerning the "proper" role for engineers as professional employees would again be found.

The findings in this chapter indicate that the importance of professional values is more highly associated with educational level than with work career patterns. This suggests either that advanced education imparts the expertise that generates the associated professional values in work settings or that the values are imparted in the more intensive socialization of graduate education. Involvement in professional activities is also most influenced by educational level, as well as technical responsibility level among the work career

FIGURE 4-1 *Organization policies for encouraging and rewarding advanced degree work by type of industry.*

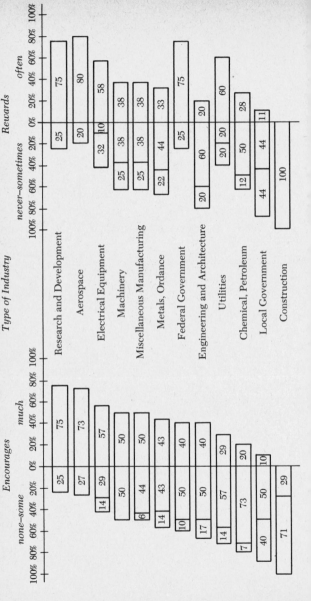

factors. There is also a clear indication of diversity among engineers in professional values, activities, and orientations.

NOTES

1. William Kornhauser, *Scientists in Industry* (Berkeley: University of California Press, 1963); Simon Marcson, *The Scientist in American Industry* (New York: Harper & Row, 1960); Barney G. Glaser, *Organizational Scientists* (Indianapolis: Bobbs-Merrill, 1964).

2. Kornhauser, *op. cit.*

3. Richard H. Hall, "The Concept of Bureaucracy: An Empirical Assessment," *American Journal of Sociology,* 69 (July 1963), 32–40.

4. Harold L. Wilensky, "The Professionalization of Everyone?" *American Journal of Sociology,* 70 (September 1964), 137–158.

5. *Ibid.*

6. William J. Goode, "Community Within a Community: The Professions," *American Sociological Review,* 22 (April 1957), 194–200; Alexander M. Carr-Sanders and P. A. Wilson, *The Professions* (Oxford: Clarendon, 1933); Talcott Parsons, "The Professions and Social Structure," in *Essays in Sociological Theory* (New York: Free Press, 1954); Everett C. Hughes, "Professions," *Daedalus,* 92 (Fall 1963), 656–660.

7. Parsons, *op. cit.*

8. Mary E. Goss, "Influence and Authority Among Physicians," *American Sociological Review,* 26 (February 1961), 39–50.

9. Gerald H. Moeller and W. W. Charters, "Relation of Bureaucratization to Sense of Power Among Teachers," *Administrative Science Quarterly,* 10 (March 1966), 444–465.

10. William M. Evan, "Role Strain and the Norm of Reciprocity in Research Organizations," *American*

Journal of Sociology, 68 (November 1962), 346–354.

11. Robert K. Merton, George C. Reader, and Patricia L. Kendall (eds.), *The Student Physician* (Cambridge, Mass.: Harvard University Press, 1957); Howard S. Becker, Blanche Geer, and Everett C. Hughes, *Boys in White: Student Culture in Medical School* (Chicago: University of Chicago Press, 1961); Goode, *op. cit.;* Donald C. Lortie, "From Laymen to Lawmen: Law School, Careers and Professional Socialization," *Harvard Educational Review*, 29 (Fall 1959), 252–269; Howard S. Becker and James Carper, "The Development of Identification With an Occupation," *American Journal of Sociology*, 61 (January 1956), 289–298.

12. Alvin W. Gouldner, "Cosmopolitans and Locals: Toward an Analysis of Latent Social Roles, I and II," *Administrative Science Quarterly*, 2 (December 1957 and March 1958), 281–306 and 444–480.

13. *Ibid.*, p. 290.

14. Donald C. Pelz, "Some Social Factors Related to Performance in a Research Organization," *Administrative Science Quarterly*, 1 (December 1956), 310–325.

15. Kornhauser, *op. cit.*, p. 130.

16. Wilensky, *op. cit.*, p. 153.

17. Barney G. Glaser, "The Local-Cosmopolitan Scientist," *American Journal of Sociology*, 69 (November 1963), 249–259.

18. Wilensky, *op. cit.*, p. 153.

19. Marcson, *op. cit.*, pp. 30–34.

5

ORGANIZATIONAL AND PROFESSIONAL CAREERS

The concept of a "career" is virtually synonymous with occupational analysis. Careers refer to the succession of stages or positions in the occupational life cycle, and the initial ones—those of recruitment and of training and socialization—have already been discussed. These, however, are but the prelude. In the mature phases of occupational life career stages assume more significance. Once one becomes a bona fide member of an occupation, what lies ahead? What are the career contingencies, the alternative occupational niches or pathways, entered into?

Historical antecedents of this process go back to the development of a master from a novice and a jour-

neyman. As for the master of a guild, so for the
contemporary professional, lifetime commitment is
expected. "So strong is this tendency that the ex-
lawyer or ex-physician is likely to be regarded rather
like an unfrocked priest, as a person who has proved
unworthy of great responsibilities." [1] But, significantly,
the engineer turned executive or sales-manager is
not so regarded. Indeed, there exists a cultural expectation that the engineer will frequently advance
to something better. Extreme statements of this view
have been voiced. For example, Wilbert E. Moore
indicates that it will necessitate a changing structure
of opportunities (which he forecasts) so that "some
engineers may end up being engineers." [2] In a similar
vein, Everett C. Hughes has remarked, "The engineer
who, at forty, can still use a slide rule or a logarithmic
table, and make a true drawing, is a failure." [3]

The legitimacy of this view might well be ques-
tioned in light of the actual nature of careers in engineering. But its bases and consequences must nevertheless be considered because it takes the form of a
self-fulfilling prophesy. As W. I. Thomas noted, facts
aside, if a situation is defined as real, it will be real
in its consequences.

The view is founded on one of the strongest ideologies in current American society. In spite of the
increasing attention on the part of social critics and
analysts to the emerging organizational society and
the new industrial state,[4] it would appear that Hora-
tio Alger is alive. (Indeed, *Strive and Succeed* has
recently been republished.) "In the American ideological baggage, the man who professes to be satisfied
has 'given up.' He has left the rat race and entered
the treadmill, where progress is foredoomed. Content-

ment is not a permissible goal; in fact it is downright immoral." [5]

Of course, the pervasiveness of an ideology of upward mobility is not a sufficient explanation of the expectation that the room at the top, which may be totally devoid of technical content, is part of an engineering career. The additional element that must be taken into account is the belief that success is to be defined in terms of organizational advancement. Although the engineer has developed accommodations between the demands of his organization and those of his profession (as was shown in the preceding chapter), the ideology under discussion reflects the view that sufficient rewards cannot be found within the social system of engineering as a profession to compete with the status of top organizational positions.

Firm Loyalty

The organizational attachment of the engineer does not involve a career-long affiliation to one firm. Rather, there is considerable mobility between organizations. Three years after graduation, eight out of ten engineers are still with their first employer, but by the time seven years have elapsed, less than half remain. Eight to eleven years after graduation, one-third have not moved, one-third have had two employers, and one-third have had three or more. Those who have been working fifteen years are equally divided between one, two, three, and four or more employers. After twenty years, the modal pattern is to have had five employers.

These patterns of mobility are likely greater than those of nonprofessional organizational personnel.[6]

Yet, they cannot be taken to imply a cosmopolitan or professional orientation. The motives for movement might be just the opposite, namely, to progress up organizational hierarchies. Inevitably, the reasons or justifications for moves will differ at various stages of the career cycle. Accordingly, the functional stages themselves must be taken into account.

Functional Stages

The basic functional categories of engineering work are those of research, development, design, operations, and management. The most striking conclusion that is suggested by Figure 5–1 is a remarkable stability

FIGURE 5–1 *Percentage of engineering graduates engaged in various functions in 1964 by years since receiving the B.S. degree.*

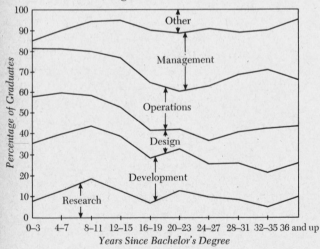

of functional specialty over the entire career. Of course, there is an increase in the managerial category with increasing age. But, for no age group—in spite of inflated titles on office doors—do as many as 30 percent claim a managerial niche. Obviously, management is *not* in fact part of the typical career in engineering in light of the pattern of work for those who graduated in the past four decades. This trend might possibly change for those who have graduated in more recent years and been exposed to revised engineering curricula. These men, at all degree levels, are more likely to begin their careers in research and development functions. To the extent that research and development is made a pathway to management —at present it does not appear to be a frequently traveled one—the proportion of engineers in management will increase. But, even if this should occur, the *typical* engineer will still not arrive in the executive suite.

Functional specialty is more clearly related to educational attainment—B.S., M.S., or Ph.D. degrees— than it is to the stage of the career cycle or time of graduation. More than one-half of B.S. degree engineers work in the area of design and operations (including production, sales, testing, and application). One-fifth of M.S. degree engineers work in similar capacities, whereas the figure for Ph.D. degree engineers is less than 10 percent. By contrast, Ph.D. degree engineers are most frequently found, as might be anticipated, in research capacities. Interestingly, the proportions of B.S., M.S., and Ph.D. degree engineers in managerial posts are essentially similar (see Figure 5–2).

Although the basic functional area of work does not vary dramatically over the various stages of the career

FIGURE 5–2 *Percentage of B.S., M.S., and Ph.D. graduates engaged in various functions in 1964.*

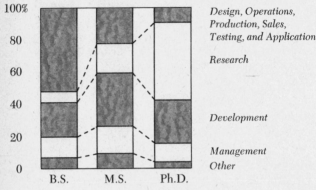

cycle, the young graduate and the man with thirty years of experience do not necessarily become involved in similar job circumstances. Major variations exist concerning the degree of technical responsibility, the amount and type of supervisory responsibility, and the balance between technical and administrative aspects of work performed.[7]

Technical Responsibility

The question of technical responsibility is based upon the distinction between the performance of standardized tasks, of complex, but recurring, tasks, and of pioneering tasks. Trends over time are most revealing. The majority of recent graduates work mainly with standardized tasks, but some ten years after graduation, the proportion relegated to such work declines to less than one-fifth. The proportion then continues to decline very gradually until, some twenty-five years after graduation, only about 10 percent remain at this level. Then, interestingly, the proportion again begins to go up. Those who graduated more than thirty-five years ago include over one-fifth limited to standardized tasks, reflecting both the constraints imposed by their dated engineering education and further obsolescence over the years.

At the other extreme, pioneering tasks are thrust upon recent graduates in less than 10 percent of the cases. However, there is a steady increase, peaking for those with twenty years of experience: about one-half of these men claim to be involved in pioneering tasks. Then the proportion lessens to but 30 percent of the oldest graduates. For all but the most recent graduates, complex, but recurring, tasks are the most frequent assignment, involving about one-half of all engineers after five years of experience (see Figure 5–3).

Once more, the highest degree attained explains considerable variation within these patterns by age. Engineers with B.S. degrees are the least likely to advance to a concentration upon pioneering tasks. For example, after some fifteen years of experience 17 percent of B.S. degree engineers are found to be working on standardized tasks and 30 percent on pioneering ones, whereas for engineers with M.S. degrees the comparable figures are 9 and 45 percent. But the greatest difference is for the Ph.D. degree engineer: after only some six years of experience 70 percent work on pioneering tasks (as compared with 9 percent of B.S. degree engineers and 28 percent of M.S. de-

FIGURE 5–3 *Percentage of graduates having various technical responsibilities in 1964 by years since receiving the B.S. degree.*

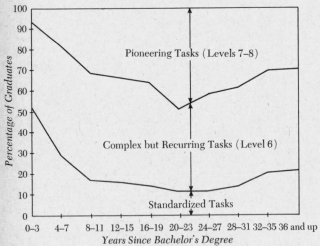

gree engineers). Indeed, for the Ph.D. degree engineer lifetime variation is limited. The doctorate via the research emphasis is the passport for remaining with pioneering pursuits.

Other research evidence dealing with scientific performance, and especially the question of "creative years" finds non-Ph.D. degree engineers not too different from Ph.D.'s in the timing of their output. Donald C. Pelz and Frank M. Andrews found engineers' contributions and usefulness reached a maximum when they were in their late forties and declined sharply after that age, with a slight recovery when they were in their late fifties. (Engineers with Ph.D. degrees had a clearer renascence in their fifties).[8]

Supervisory Responsibility

The assumption of supervisory responsibility might be considered an indirect indicator of managerial-type work, albeit lacking the managerial title in many instances. Patterns here are different from those found with regard to technical responsibility.

The majority of graduates begin with no supervisory responsibility, although two-fifths begin with the supervision of nonprofessional personnel. After twelve years of experience, one-third are involved with the supervision of professional personnel. The most consistent pattern is that for the supervision of management personnel, which increases over the entire career cycle, involving one-fourth of those with sixteen years of experience and gradually increasing up to one-third of those who have been serving in their occupational capacities for thirty-five years.

Consistent with the pattern shown to be associated with the holding of a managerial position, a high degree of managerial responsibility is not highly related to the holding of advanced degrees. However, engineers with B.S. degrees do differ from those holding M.S. and Ph.D. degrees, while the latter two groups are remarkably similar to each other. Engineers with M.S. and Ph.D. degrees are more likely to be responsible for the supervision of professional personnel than are engineers with B.S. degrees, but they are *not* more often involved in the supervision of management personnel.

Administrative Work

An additional indicator of changes incurred during the career cycle is that of the balance between an emphasis upon technical work as contrasted with administrative work. The transformation that occurs over the years in this balance probably accounts for the commonly held managerial expectations. The context of both technical and administrative work will vary over the career, the nature of this alteration involving the previously discussed factors of the complexity of technical tasks performed and the levels of supervisory responsibility subsumed in administrative work. Administration, however, refers not only to supervision of personnel; at one extreme, it may be defined as paper work, and at the other extreme, it may be defined as high-level decision making.

The increasing significance of administrative work over the career is impressive. A primarily administrative responsibility is claimed by less than 5 percent of the youngest graduates, the proportion growing to two-fifths of those who have had twenty-five years of experience. The contrast of those whose work is at least half administrative with those whose work is entirely or primarily technical is even more dramatic: whereas over three-fourths of the young graduates are involved in the technical realm, almost an equal proportion of those with twenty-five years of experience describe at least half of their duties as being administrative. (For the remaining period of work-life, the figure drops to two-thirds on the administrative side.)

The contrast of Ph.D., M.S., and B.S. degree engineers yet again indicates disparate career lines for the three groups. The engineer with a Ph.D. degree who is typically working upon pioneering tasks in research or development is in a primarily administrative capacity in only 12 percent of the cases. The proportion of primarily administrative M.S. and B.S. degree engineers is twice as large. The combined category of primarily administrative work and half administrative-half technical work accounts for only 31 percent of the Ph.D. degree engineers as compared to the 47 percent of the M.S. degree engineers and 53 percent of the B.S. degree engineers who do this.

B.S. vs. Ph.D. Degree Engineers

The alternative career paths of the B.S. and the Ph.D. degree engineer (the M.S. degree engineer being a curious intermediate case, not consistently closer to either extreme) reflect contingencies derived initially from differing socialization experiences in engineering schools and, subsequently, exposure to contrasting organizational structures. The B.S. degree engineer is in many ways the essence of the organization man. For, although he is a professional, this is largely due to his occupation having professional status in the larger society. He lacks exclusive jurisdiction to his field of specialization—so much so that a higher proportion of B.S. degree physicists call themselves engineers than do B.S. degree engineers.[9] Most important, he does not hold to professional norms of behavior that conflict with the organizational setting within which his attainment goals are cast.

The situation of the engineer with a Ph.D. degree is more complicated. His allegiance to professional norms is greater, reflecting not only his socialization but also the possibility of pursuing the research function of a professional within an organizational context. Yet, this possibility is limited, given the poorly articulated nature of professional goals within the social system of engineering (Does the Ph.D. degree engineer think of himself as an engineer or a scientist?) and confounded by the still experimental nature of professional ladders in industry.

Creativity

Throughout this discussion on "ways to the top," the emphasis has been upon pathways in organizational settings, whether in terms of actual promotion or through changes less clearly proclaimed, as, for example, assuming increasing responsibilities. This emphasis follows from the social definitions and expectations concerning engineering careers, as well as from the fundamental fact of the engineers' orientation (most obviously in the case of non-Ph.D. degree engineers) being upon status rather than science.

However, recent findings that deal with the question of productive climates for research and development of engineers and scientists in organizations suggest that such an analysis needs to be taken further. Subtle measures of the productivity of engineers and scientists reveal that such "obvious" factors as an individual's dedication, his having supportive supervisors, and his orientation toward science, rather than toward an organization, are not in all cases the crucial factors predictive of the payoff from creative potential.[10] In this context, Pelz and Andrews specify the conditions that enhance the yield from creative ability as: "working on a project or specializing in an area for a relatively short time; being part of a work team where coordination was not too high, and where one had the ability to influence important decision-makers; and having reasonably good facilities for communicating new ideas to others." [11]

The most perplexing issue regarding creativity concerns its place in the organizational society. The act of creation (as described in *The Act of Creation*,[12] one of the most brilliant books of the past decade) implies the *private* domain of the great men of the world's cultural history. Yet they, too, were immersed in social systems. Thus, for the contemporary engineer, acts of creation might be thought of as anti-systems. At the private level of individual motivation, one can think of the engineer whose definition of success is not that of top organizational rungs but, instead, of technical achievement. But he cannot escape the fact that organizations are striving to institutionalize creativity. Nor can he escape the demands for signs of attainment (most obviously salary) that his family, his community, and even his employer impose upon the least status-minded engineer.

Fame

Although it is true that all professionals employed in large organizations share numerous problems in the conflicting systems of organizations and professions, the situation of engineers in industry is extreme, and a comparison with scientists is highly salutary. The most important contrast lies in science having developed a complex social system in its own right. (It is not accidental that there is a well-developed sociology of science but almost no sociology of engineering.)

The social system of science involves little ambiguity concerning professional identity. The criteria of success are also not obscure. The Valhalla of science

is well known within the scientific community,[13] in
the intellectual and academic community, and among
the informed public as well. But what of fame in
engineering? What are the prominent names—Watt,
Hoover, and who?

Alternative models of attainment for engineers
would therefore seem to require either passing as a
scientist or attaining local kudos within the firm by
climbing its ladder—and, in many instances, abandon-
ing engineering work. The situation is one involving a
vicious cycle. Because of the public image of engineering work—respectable scientific-type work, without the lengthy preparation required in most professions, leading to managerial positions—individuals
with values consistent with this image are attracted.
The managerial bias may be attenuated in engineering school in its technical-scientific emphasis, but it
is by no means extinguished. Indeed, the individual
whose initial orientation was technical is likely to be
influenced by his classmates' views of climbing organizational ladders. More often than not, engineers
enter industry with nonprofessional goals.[14] They tend
to "feel that their future lies somewhere in the country's industrial system, but do not think of any com-
pany (no matter what its specialty) or any position
impossible for them." [15] Such expectations are not
altered by subsequent experience in industry, nor are
they undermined by professional activities.

In the context of industrial employment, organizational goals will, naturally, be emphasized. Even
though a majority of engineers cling to some professional norms—for example, to have considerable
freedom to manage their own work—managerial personnel do not recognize such norms as being important for engineering employees.

Experiments in industry with the development of professional career ladders have had uncertain results —uncertain both for industry and for engineering professionalism. A provocative analysis of this type of system has presented the argument that although special professional ladders, or dual ladders, have generally been viewed as provided by organizations in response to pressures from professionals, they might well be viewed as created by management. "Management thus attempts to impose professionalism as a definition of success within the organization in order to maintain commitment on the part of those specialists who would ordinarily be considered failures for not having moved into management. Identification as a professional has become a way to redefine failure as success." [16]

This thesis is a significant one. It is unmistakably applicable to salesmen, for whom any pretention of professionalism is inappropriate. But to the extent that engineering has legitimate professional goals— most clearly seen in the case of Ph.D. degree engineers —it cannot be assumed to be the prevailing mechanism. Above all, the possibility that professionalism *might* be a way of redefining failure as success indicates one thing: the absence of clear occupational goals and the ambiguous definition of success in engineering.

NOTES

1. Theodore Caplow, *The Sociology of Work* (Minneapolis: University of Minnesota Press, 1954), p. 106.
2. Moore's forecast is in terms of "relations experts" being

most likely to capture top corporation posts in the future. See Wilbert E. Moore, *The Conduct of the Corporation* (New York: Vintage, 1962), p. 173.

3. Everett C. Hughes, *Men and their Work* (New York: Free Press, 1958), p. 137.

4. See, for example, William H. Whyte, Jr., *The Organization Man* (New York: Simon and Schuster, 1956); Robert Presthus, *The Organizational Society* (New York: Vintage, 1965); John Kenneth Galbraith, *The New Industrial State* (Boston: Houghton Mifflin, 1967).

5. Moore, *op. cit.*, p. 175. Cf. Galbraith, *op. cit.*, Chap. 32.

6. Cf. J. E. Gerstl and S. P. Hutton, *Engineers: The Anatomy of a Profession* (London: Tavistock Publications, 1966), pp. 94–99.

7. See pp. 104–106 in Chapter 4 above for specific job descriptions used.

8. Donald C. Pelz and Frank M. Andrews, *Scientists in Organizations* (New York: Wiley, 1966), Chap. 10.

9. National Opinion Research Center, *The United States College-educated Population: 1960,* Report 102 (Chicago: University of Chicago, October 1965), pp. 72–75.

10. Pelz and Andrews, *op. cit.*, Chap. 9.

11. *Ibid.*, p. 171.

12. Arthur Koestler, *The Act of Creation* (New York: Macmillan, 1964).

13. Stephen Cole and Jonathan Cole, "Scientific Output and Recognition," *American Sociological Review,* 32 (June 1967), 377–390.

14. Fred H. Goldner and R. R. Ritti, "Professionalization as Career Immobility," *American Journal of Sociology,* 72 (March 1967), 489–502.

15. Howard S. Becker and James Carper, "The Elements of Identification with an Occupation," *American Sociological Review,* 21 (June 1956), 341–348.

16. Goldner and Ritti, *op. cit.*, p. 490.

6

FAMILY, CAREER, AND OCCUPATIONAL COMMUNITY

In the preceding chapters an understanding of the occupational role of the engineer and the engineering profession has been sought—by examining events associated with recruitment to the profession; with educational patterns and problems; with involvement in, and commitment to, the profession; and with the constraints of the career. This focus upon the public world of the engineer has produced a picture of great diversity in the motivations, experiences, and values of those who have chosen to be called engineers.

Yet, the public world of the engineer presents only a partial picture of this occupation, it neglects the private world of the citizen, father, and husband. The interplay between the public and the private world of the engineer reveals the significance of the world of work and the manner in which work is influenced and impinged upon by extra-work considerations. Some occupational careers, for example, are pursued in considerable isolation from the family, making few demands upon the family members beyond those that are already an integral part of our culture, such as scheduling meals, leisure, and home location in accordance with work-time and work-place. Other occupations, however, make great demands upon family members, requiring the active participation of wife and children in the career activities of the husband.

Another reason for exploring the private world of the engineer goes beyond simply providing a fuller description of an occupational role. Early in this book it was suggested that one of the reasons for studying the engineer was connected with the growing centrality of engineering activities in American society. More specifically, this centrality will go beyond the provision of technological innovations that have indirect consequences for people, to the establishment of planned, directed social systems with very direct consequences. The scientists and engineers who plan such systems will, of course, require very special technical knowledge. They will also need to be acutely aware and sensitive to the nature of social institutions and the meaning of human values. Some of this understanding can be obtained by exposure to those disciplines that make human behavior their subject; much of it can be obtained by being a part of the society they seek to shape.

In reflecting on this matter one cannot help but be painfully aware of how little is known of the values, attitudes, and personal philosophies of those men whose activities affect the lives of millions. Images in this connection are highly affected by the mass media, which by and large project extreme stereotypes of the new men of science. On one hand, there is Dr. Strangelove, a misanthrope whose physical infirmities mirror his crippled inner spirit and lack of love, respect, or understanding for his fellow-men. At the other extreme, there is the magazine cover scientist who is a kind of super American, exhibiting all the civic, social, intellectual virtues of our culture. Both images are not of this world and therefore serve to dispel any real fears about those who use science and technology for the good of society. Yet, the technocratic impulse in engineering is very clear, and it is important to know something of the engineer's contact with his own society. Is he a member of his community, participating in its civic, political, and cultural life? Or, is he a member of a closed community of engineers, living out their lives within the expanding boundaries of the organization?

In the remainder of this chapter, the interplay between the public and private life of the engineer will be explored. The focus will be upon (1) work and the family—the extent to which the demands of work impinge upon the pattern of life in the family, (2) career and community—the extent to which life in the organization takes on characteristics of a pseudo-community that limits participation in the real community, and (3) leisure and occupational community —the cultural and social life of the engineer.

Work and Family

The specific concern with the way in which work influences life in the family can be traced to the more general concern with the relationship between industrialization and the structure of the family. In a most influential essay on this subject, Talcott Parsons has argued that one of the requirements of industrialization is a population that is socially and geographically mobile, committed to rationality and universalistic norms, and motivated to fill occupational roles on the basis of achievement standards of technical competence.[1] These requirements are best met within the context of the dominant form of the American nuclear, structurally isolated family, which is not incorporated into larger descent groups or extended families and which has greater parent-child, than conjugal, solidarity.

From this general conception, a view of the family as an instrumental resource in the work-life of its members can be obtained. Loose familial ties make mobility possible by loosening the psychological bonds responsible for mental immobility. Close ties, on the other hand, make leaving the family difficult because one's main identification is with an established status group rather than with a status group in which one aspires to hold membership. Moreover, decisions involved in the formation of a new family are also closely tied to the demands of the work role and the anticipated changes in that work role. The choice of a mate among business leaders is found to be highly patterned and to be closely tied to the career advancement of successful men.[2] Similarly, the timing of marriage and childbearing among engineers is found to be associated with educational and occupational mobility. For example, those working on advanced degrees are found to marry later and have their children at longer time intervals.[3]

The extent to which there is a close link between work and the family is found to be associated with the particular setting in which one is employed and the level of one's occupation. Males whose occupational development (for example, promotion and wages) is quite determinate, as in unionized occupations, are less likely to draw their families into career-related decisions, leaving the family as less democratic with respect to power and decision making. Males employed in bureaucratic settings are more likely to have wives who perceive that they play an effective role in family mobility and thereby show more power in family decision-making situations.[4] This suggests, of course, that the engineering career, which runs its course in the large organization, should also influence life in the family.

Several aspects of this view of the way work influences the family have not gone unchallenged. Eugene Litwak, in response to Parson's view of the isolated nuclear family, has suggested the existence of a modified extended family that gives aid to family members, maintains contact with other family members, and generally provides supportive behavior that becomes an aid rather than hindrance to social and geographical mobility.[5]

Similarly, there are exceptions to the alleged close connection between the public and private lives of organization men. One of the business leaders interviewed by William Lloyd Warner and James C. Abegglen was asked if his wife played an instrumental role in his career. He answered:

Definitely not. I believe she would agree with me that the only way she helped is by doing a good job of raising our children so that I don't have to take time out to straighten out a bunch of brats, and by doing a minimum of griping because I am home so little. . . . I've kept my home life completely separate from business always. My wife has never met my business associates' wives, and never will, if I can help it! [6]

Another manager expresses the view of the home as a haven to be protected from the demands of the organization and the career. He said:

Mrs. Hayes doesn't have time for afternoon bridge parties or cocktail parties; we don't go to night clubs. Certain things creep into a man's life that way, and you begin to worry about what each is doing. You can't work that way. It usually ends in a broken home. I don't think you can burn the candle at both ends. [7]

Turning to some of the details of the family life of the engineer, findings show that they are very much married and producers of families: 90 percent of the engineers are presently married (about 2 percent are separated, divorced, or widowed) and 80 percent of them have one or more children. Reasonably large families are also quite frequent, approximately 23 percent have three children and 17 percent have four or more children.

The marital choices of engineers in terms of the educational status of their wives reflect the mobile character of those who enter the profession, as discussed in Chapter 2. Compared to the educational level of his parents, that of the engineer's spouse is considerably higher; approximately 60 percent of the wives have at least some college. The pattern in these marital choices suggests that engineers marry "up" educationally with reference to their parents educational origins, but they tend to marry "down" with reference to their own educational attainments.

	Father	*Mother*	*Spouse*
Eighth grade or less	34	28	—
Some high school	17	17	8
High school graduate	19	31	32
Some college	13	15	29
Bachelor's degree	12	8	26
Master's degree	3	1	4
Doctor's degree	2	—	—

Although it is difficult to determine from these data whether engineers married up or down with respect to the occupational status of the spouse's father, it is probably safe to assume that the spouses who had no college experience (40 percent) are not very likely to be from professional or high business origins. Thus, for a sizable proportion of engineers their own upwardly mobile behavior, with respect to occupational and educational achievements, is not similarly reflected in their choice of a mate.

The nature of the interplay between family and career for the engineer is perhaps best revealed when he is asked to make a choice between family requirements and the demands of the career. When asked to indicate which of six things is most important to them personally, 47 percent indicated "family relationships" and another 30 percent selected "professional career" as most important to them personally. This indicates that family and career combined account for the things of central importance to engineers, with more emphasis upon the family when he is forced to make a choice. When engineers were asked to make the same choice between family and career, only this time in terms of what they "think is most important to the typical engineer," 58 percent indicated that most engineers think the professional career is most important and 27 percent thought that most engineers would select family relationships as most important. The disparity between personal values and those attributed to other engineers probably reflects some degree of personal conflict over the competing demands of family and career.

A classification of engineers' personal values with those values attributed to other engineers reveals four distinct types: those who value the family and think most engineers value the family; those who value the family but think most engineers value the career; those who value the career but think most engineers value the family; and those who value the career and think most engineers also value the career.[8] This pattern is presented below with the number of engineers fitting each pattern:

	Values		
Self	Others	Number	Percent
Family	Family	631	31
Family	Career	565	28
Career	Family	65	3
Career	Career	756	38
		2017	100

Clearly, those who personally value the professional career also overwhelmingly view other engineers as quite similar to themselves, whereas those who personally value the family are more likely to perceive themselves as members of a profession whose practitioners have dissimilar values with respect to family and career. The particular family-career type that an engineer exemplifies also seems to be associated with the level of education of his spouse. Engineers who personally value the career are much more likely to have a spouse with a bachelor's degree or higher than are engineers who personally value the family over the career. This may suggest that part of the conflict that faces the family-oriented engineer can be traced to the lower education of his spouse.

Career-oriented engineers are more likely than family-oriented engineers to hold positions of lower technical responsibility, to be colleague oriented, to be involved in professional societies and activities, and to let few obstacles stand in the way of accepting a new and better position. It is tempting to respond to these findings by simply concluding that family commitments conflict with the requirements of the occupational career and thereby subject the engineer to greater personal stress and poor occupational performance. An equally plausible hypothesis is that the family orientation of engineers did not *precede* their lower professional performance but, instead, followed an inadequate career development as an adaptation or an ego-maintaining alternative to the career. Although this hypothesis cannot be examined with the data on hand, the notion of family-career conflict should be examined within the framework of stages of career and stages of the family, where the demands each orientation makes upon the engineer may be quite varied.

Another way to examine the interplay between work and the family, which does not require a forced choice between work and family, is to contrast the extent to which certain family-related values are held by engineers and the extent to which they can satisfy these values within the framework of their position and their organization. Table 6–1 indicates the responses to questions concerning family values in terms of their importance to engineers and how likely it is that the value can be satisfied in their present position.

TABLE 6-1 *Responses of Engineers to Family Values in Terms of Importance and Characteristic of Their Position**

Values	Importance			Characteristic of Present Position		
	Very	Some	None	Very	Some	None
A position that leaves sufficient time to devote to my family	59%	39%	2%	37%	59%	4%
To be able to take time off with the family without worrying about the work I'm not doing	28	54	18	19	61	20
To be able to spend more time with my family as my career progresses	17	58	25	6	59	35
To be assured that I won't be moving about the country	24	45	31	26	48	26
To work in a company that realizes that a man has responsibilities to his family as well as his work	49	46	5	29	64	7

* $N = 3217$.

Only two of the five family values are very important to one-half or more of the engineers, with the other three values showing much less in the way of importance. The largest discrepancies between the "importance" and "characteristic" response to the values also occur for the two value items that are important to the largest proportion of engineers.

The discrepancy between the importance of a family value and the chances of achieving that family value can be treated as an index of the degree of conflict between family and work. With this conception in mind, average discrepancy scores were computed for each engineer across the five value items. The highest discrepancy scores were obtained for engineers who hold middle-level positions with respect to supervisory and technical responsibility and for engineers who had experienced the greatest amount of intergenerational mobility. Such findings seem to be quite consistent with the view expressed earlier that persons in different career stages might well experience different degrees of "stress" with respect to the conflicting demands of family and career. Engineers at middle levels of managerial and technical responsibility may possibly be "men on the way to the top," who have been singled out for their potential for upper managerial positions. Although they are in a career stage that promises greater advancement, there may also be greater pressure to give an inordinate amount of time to one's career—much more than one would give if he had little chance for advancement or had already achieved a high position. The higher discrepancy scores of the most mobile engineers would also be consistent with a view that mobile men are subjected to multiple pressures that are due to the loss of stable friendship and familial ties and the need to establish ties with persons that they may have less in common with socially and culturally. Such pressures seem to be present both for the mobile man and his wife. For example, Peter Blau suggests that mobile persons "are marginal men, in some respects out of tune with others both in their new and original strata in the occupational hierarchy." [9] In addition, Robert P. Stuckert found that the wives of mobile men tended to be social isolates with little involvement in extended family relations.[10]

Career and Community

In 1956 William H. Whyte, Jr., described the "rootlessness" of the geographically and socially mobile organization men.[11] Not only have the organization men lost their ties with families and communities where they have spent the major part of their lives, but also their numerous long-distance moves between college, new positions, and new employers serve to exacerbate their sense of not belonging. The problems associated with the transient life are described by Whyte:

One of the dangers in the transient life is that these young people, because they must move about so frequently, will more and more identify their total destiny with one particular organization. For society as well as for themselves, the organization transients need to multiply their allegiances—to the church, to community, and the life. These additional allegiances provoke no great ideological conflicts with the office, certainly, but they do turn the executive away from complete preoccupation with one encompassing organization.[12]

The view expressed by Whyte tends to place the greatest stress upon social mobility and the endless cycle of "moving in and moving out," which produces a personality that adapts by avoiding close relationships and enduring commitments to people and places. This is probably an important part of how the engineer relates to the community in which he lives, but it tends to be very one-sided in its perspective. It neglects, for example, the direct role that an organization might play in encouraging or discouraging participation in local community affairs, as a way by which organizations seek to protect their interests. It also neglects the possibility that the type of involvement an organization man has with his community is a continuation of a set of personal and social patterns that existed prior to his entry into any organization (although these patterns may still be due to the fact that engineers are socially mobile).

A study of approximately 1000 engineering graduates of the University of California at Los Angeles and Berkeley sought to determine the degree of continuity that exists between the engineer's life as a student and his life as an engineer.[13] Engineers who were more involved in college life when they were students were also more involved in such post-college activities as chambers of commerce, religious organizations, fraternal orders, and political parties. In most cases this involvement was especially pronounced for that group of students that was high on participation in college life but low on academic achievement. Such students were classified as "collegiates," and they were found to be the highest participants in community life after college. The students who were high on academic performance and low on participation in college life—

classified as the "grinds"—were least likely to be
involved in community life. These findings suggest
that the particular patterns of adaptation to community life, described above by Whyte, are perhaps
set in motion before the engineer actually moves into
a position in an organization.

Turning to the role that an organization plays in
influencing its members' participation in community
affairs, there seem to be conflicting views on the
direction and extent of influence. In a study of executives from absentee-owned corporations, Roland J.
Pellegrin and Charles H. Coates have suggested that
there is a close link between the executive's career and
his involvement in community organizations.[14] Executives from absentee-owned corporations were involved
in the most powerful community organizations, and
they were also involved in national and state organizations. Most likely, such patterns of involvement can
be traced both to the fact that corporations "assigned"
their executives to civic organizations and to the desire
of executives to compensate for their lack of personal
power and wealth in the organizations in which they
are employed.

A contrary view is expressed by Robert O. Schulze.
He argues that with urbanization and the growth of
organizations there is less dependence upon the local
community and that the power of local community
organizations is less relevant as a corporation is national in orientation and interests.[15] Schulze under-
takes an examination of the role of economic dominants (those with top roles in largest industries and
banks and the largest property owners) of a midwestern industrial community of 20,000 residents for
the period from 1823 to 1955. The data indicate that
"the historical drift has been characterized by a with-

drawal of economic dominants from active and overt participation in public life." [16]

The degree of involvement of engineers in political and civic affairs in their community during the past year (the survey was conducted in 1965) is indicated in Table 6–2. The activity items are ordered as follows: from those that most engineers indicated active participation to those in which few engineers were involved. First, considering political activities, there seems to be a sharp distinction between activities that reflect active, personal involvement and those that reflect less visible, less personal political activity. Also, those activities most frequently checked (the first five items) do not require a public statement of political position. Signing petitions, giving money, and writing letters, on the other hand, do involve a public statement of political position, and such activities might possibly be frowned upon by organizations because they have the potential for alienating community members of different political leanings.

A somewhat similar pattern may be seen for civic affairs as well, although the demarcation between active and passive involvement is not as sharp as it is for political activities. Nonetheless, about one-fourth or fewer engineers report direct involvement in civic affairs that reflect a commitment to a position, program, or issue.

These data easily testify to the general "apolitical" nature of engineers whose involvement in large, image-conscious organizations heavily immersed in federal contracts serves to discourage active political behavior.[17] Such limited involvement, however, may also be due to the "depoliticized" education of the engineers (discussed in Chapter 3), and to the transient nature of their occupational life, which dis-

TABLE 6–2   *Engineers' Participation in Political and*

Politics	Participation
I followed current national and international events in the newspapers daily and magazines weekly.	95%
I discussed political issues with my friends.	94
I voted in the last national election.	87
I voted in the last primary or local election.	87
I listened at least once a month to speeches and discussion programs on radio or TV dealing with national and international problems.	86
I signed a petition for or against some legislation.	39
I read one or more books about politics.	37
I contributed money to some political cause or group.	33
I wrote a letter or sent a telegram to a public official.	20
I participated in the activities of a political group.	14
I collected money for some political cause or group.	6
I ran for or held an elective office sometime during the past four years.	4

courages community involvement. In order to explore
these possibilities further, the extent of involvement
in political and civic affairs of engineers who have
experienced different community moving patterns and
of engineers who are in positions of varying responsibility in their organizations can be examined.

Tables 6–3 and 6–4 show the involvement in political and civic activities of engineers who spend different amounts of time on their work during their non-
work hours and of engineers who have experienced
different job mobility patterns. The literature discussed
earlier would suggest that both engineers who devote

*Civic Activities in Their Community During Past Year**

Civic Affairs	*Participation*
I gave money to the community chest or fund.	90%
I followed local events regularly in my newspaper.	87
I belonged to a labor union, businessmen's association, or professional society.	56
I talked with my neighbors about practical ways in which our neighborhood might be made better, for example, pleasanter, friendlier.	50
I was a member of a community organization, such as the PTA, Citizens Association.	42
I attended meetings of some local civic group.	38
I had some contact with a local official about a local civic problem.	26
I taught, or helped in some other direct way, a volunteer young peoples' group, such as scouts, YMCA.	25
I served on a volunteer committee for more community service.	15
I collected money or carried a petition for some local civic cause.	15
I wrote a letter to the newspaper about some community problems.	5

* N = 3217.

more time to their work while at home and those who have experienced more job mobility should be less involved in community activities. The data on political activities clearly do not support either of these hypotheses. If anything, engineers who spend more hours on work-related matters at home show a slight tendency to be more involved in political activities, and engineers who have had more employers also tend to be more involved in political activities. However, these differences are quite small, and the main findings do not support our expectations. The same general pattern is also apparent for civic activities (see Table 6–4). Engineers who work more hours at home and those who have had more employers during their career were also the ones who were more likely to be involved in more civic activities. The differences are again quite small, but the important point is that there is no support for the hypothesis that selected aspects of work and career limit organization members from becoming involved in community political and civic activities.

A closer look at some of the demands of the professional career may provide a better picture of the manner in which the career influences community life. Tables 6–5 and 6–6 show the involvement in political and civic activities of engineers who hold positions of varying supervisory and technical responsibility. The data clearly indicate that the higher the supervisory and technical responsibility of the engineer, the more he is involved in political and civic activities in the community. These findings provide support for the Pellegrin and Coates study, which found executives of absentee-owned corporations to be more involved in powerful community organizations. However, the findings are contrary to Schulze's view that local community involvement is less important for organizations as they become national in orientation and interests.

The overall pattern of findings with respect to involvement in community affairs suggests that such involvement is more than a simple function of the extent to which organizations encourage or discourage their employees from becoming involved in their communities. The fact that engineers who moved more during their career and who spend more hours working at home were also those who were more

TABLE 6–3 Extent of Involvement in Political Activities by Hours Working at Home and Job Mobility

Number of Political Activities	Hours Spent Working at Home Each Week				Number of Employers During Career					
	None	1–3	4–6	7 or more	1	2	3	4	5	6 or more
0–5	50%	43%	37%	38%	44%	39%	39%	38%	40%	40%
6–7	34	42	40	42	39	42	40	44	35	42
8–9	11	12	17	16	11	15	14	15	20	14
10–12	4	5	6	4	6	4	6	3	5	3
Number of Engineers	700	1293	807	425	1097	745	556	303	205	227

TABLE 6–4 Extent of Involvement in Civic Activities by Hours Working at Home and Job Mobility

Number of Civic Activities	Hours Spent Working at Home Each Week				Number of Employers During Career					
	None	1–3	4–6	7 or more	1	2	3	4	5	6 or more
0–3	52%	37%	29%	35%	41%	38%	35%	35%	36%	36%
4–5	29	31	34	32	30	33	32	30	32	33
6–7	13	20	22	21	19	19	21	24	20	16
8–11	6	11	15	11	10	10	13	11	12	15
Number of Engineers	700	1293	807	425	1097	745	556	303	205	227

TABLE 6-5 *Extent of Involvement in Political Activities by Supervisory and Technical Responsibility*

Number of Political Activities	Supervisory Responsibility*			Technical Responsibility*		
	1	2–4	5–9	1–5	6	7–8
0–5	49%	41%	35%	53%	39%	36%
6–7	36	42	43	34	43	41
8–9	12	12	17	10	13	18
10–12	4	5	6	4	4	6
Number of Engineers	916	870	1331	648	1506	941

* See Chapter 4 for a description of the supervisory and technical responsibility categories.

TABLE 6–6 *Extent of Involvement in Civic Activities by Supervisory and Technical Responsibility*

Number of Civic Activities	Supervisory Responsibility*			Technical Responsibility*		
	1	2–4	5–9	1–5	6	7–8
0–3	48%	40%	28%	47%	37%	32%
4–5	30	31	33	29	33	32
6–7	14	19	24	17	19	22
8–11	6	10	15	7	11	14
Number of Engineers	916	870	1331	648	1506	941

* See Chapter 4 for a description of the supervisory and technical responsibility categories.

involved in the community suggests that some employees accomplish more in the limited time available to them than others who have more time to devote to the community. This is reminiscent of a particular type of engineering student who manages to spend more time on social, cultural, and sports activities at the university than other engineering students and still obtain higher grades.[18]

But involvement in the community is also more than simply a matter of a driving, high energy personality type who does more of everything in less time than other mere mortals. The data also suggest that the extent to which a person is involved in his community depends upon the particular career stage in which he finds himself. The fact that engineers with high technical and supervisory positions are more involved in the community may suggest that they are in a stage of their career when both the family and the career are less demanding and they therefore have more time for community activities. On the other hand, engineers in the lower positions may also be at stages in their careers when more time must be devoted to work if they hope to achieve higher technical or supervisory positions. The total result is that the family, career, and community may be viewed as making competing demands upon the professional's time, and the demands of each change in importance for different stages in the professional's career.

Leisure and Occupational Community

The final concern in the interplay between the private and public life of the engineer is with the kind of exposure he has to his society through leisure pursuits and the extent to which he participates in a "closed

community" of technical experts. This interest is based
on the assumption that engineers are now, and will
increasingly be in the future, involved in technical
decisions that require understanding of human affairs
and social problems obtained through formal education, reading, and direct experience. The previous section noted that engineers have a very distinct pattern
of minimal direct involvement in the affairs of the
communities in which they live. As shown in Chapter
3, engineering education also provides limited exposure to those disciplines whose subject matter is
concerned with the human condition.

Table 6–7 indicates the general periodical reading
habits of engineers. They are least likely to read
periodicals that deal with contemporary issues in social and political life—a reading pattern that is quite
consistent with the earlier data on participation in
political and civic affairs. The dominant reading pattern in terms of extensive exposure is found for general
news magazines and general interest magazines and
digests. The type of reading done by engineers outside of their technical reading is very similar to that
found by Harold L. Wilensky, who found that engineers, as compared with lawyers and professors, read
fewer "quality" newspapers and magazines and watch
fewer "educational" and "special" programs on television. In fact, their television viewing patterns are
more likely to be classified as indiscriminant viewing.
In general, Wilensky finds the media consuming patterns of engineers to be closer to what he terms the
"middle mass." [19]

Similar results on the reading habits of engineering
graduates of a larger midwestern university were obtained. When asked to indicate the three most frequently read periodicals, engineers mentioned *Time*,

TABLE 6–7   *Periodicals Read During the Past Year**

	Extent of Reading		
Periodical	*Exten- sive*	*Occa- sional*	*Rarely or Never*
General science (e.g., *Scientific American; Science*)	20%	57%	23%
Business and management (e.g., *Business Week; Fortune*)	26	55	18
Political commentary (e.g., *New Republic; National Review; Nation*)	7	34	60
Essay (e.g., *Harpers; Atlantic Monthly*)	4	26	70
General interest (e.g., *Life; Look*)	36	57	7
Digests (e.g., *Reader's Digest*)	32	50	18
Sports (e.g., *Sports Illustrated*)	17	48	35
Hobby (e.g., *Popular Mechanics*)	18	46	36
Family magazines (e.g., *Better Homes and Gardens*)	13	55	31
Daily newspaper	92	8	1
General news (e.g., *Time; Newsweek*)	58	38	4
Men's magazines (e.g., *Playboy; Adventure*)	8	43	48

* N = 3117.

Life, and *Reader's Digest,* respectively. This pattern
was the same for all engineers regardless of their field
of study or the extent of their formal education. The
number of engineers reading any "quality" periodicals
is also very low. Of the 2,245 engineers participating
in the study, 169 read *Scientific American,* 41 read
Science, 38 read *Harper's,* 36 read *Atlantic Monthly,*
33 read *Saturday Review,* 29 read *International Science
and Technology,* 22 read *National Review,* and 16 read
Harvard Business Review.[20]

Participation in other general cultural activities by engineers also reveals a mixed pattern, with some tendency toward the middle mass consuming behavior. Considering such events as plays and concerts, a little more than 50 percent of a national sample of engineers had attended a play during the past year and about 40 percent had attended a musical concert. Generally, less than 10 percent were any more actively involved in literary, dramatic, or musical activities, such as attending a lecture by an author, contributing money or time to a local musical enterprise, or reading books about music. In the area of art, about 33 percent had attended an art show during the past year and about 10 percent had read books about art, artists, or art history.

Turning to the nature of the engineer's formal work associations and social life, some idea of his place in an occupational community can be obtained. The existence of occupational community among engineers would be conducive to the emergence of a strong colleague orientation which is essential to any profession.[21] However, a pronounced pattern of occupational community might also be indicative of a certain "narrowness" of professional perspective, which cuts the engineer off from the society that he believes he understands in many of his system design activities. This points to one of the dilemmas of professional occupations—they constantly face the possibility that they will turn too much attention inward to the profession itself, forgetting their mission to serve people or society. Thus, occupational community can have its noble, as well as its defensive, purposes.

At work, engineers tend to have considerable contact with other engineers, with over 90 percent reporting daily to weekly contact. Approximately 66 percent report such frequent contact with engineering technicians and middle management, whereas over 50 percent have daily to weekly contact with lower management and skilled workers. Table 6–8 shows the patterns of social associations that engineers have with other persons in various occupational groups.

Involvement in social associations is shown to be much lower than contacts on the job. The highest pro-

TABLE 6–8 *Engineers' Social Activities Outside of Work with Other Personnel in Their Organization**

	Extent of Social Contact		
Personnel Group	*Daily-Weekly*	*Monthly to Once a Year*	*Did Not Contact*
Top management			
(President; Vice President)	5%	43%	52%
Middle management			
(managers of departments)	19	62	19
Lower management (foremen)	13	54	34
Engineers in your own field	39	56	5
Engineers in allied fields	30	61	9
Engineering technicians	16	52	32
Computer programers	6	28	66
Mathematicians	6	34	60
Physical scientists	11	43	46
Biological scientists	7	38	56
Lawyers	8	45	46
Social scientists	3	24	72
Librarians	2	20	78
Clerical personnel	16	48	37
Skilled workers	19	52	28
Semiskilled workers	14	46	40

* $N = 3117$.

portions of daily to weekly social contact is with other
engineers, followed by skilled workers, middle management, engineering technicians, and clerical personnel.
There is relatively little social contact with top management, social scientists, librarians, mathematicians, and
computer programers.

These patterns remain pretty much the same for
engineers in different technical and supervisory responsibilities. Engineers with high and low technical
responsibility showed very similar social contacts with
all occupational groups. There was some tendency for
engineers in high supervisory positions to have less
social contact with engineers and other personnel of
lower organizational status and more contact with
management persons than did engineers holding positions of low supervisory responsibility. (These data
are not shown.)

A better picture of how work associations influence
social associations can be obtained by looking at the
patterns of social contact for engineers who do and
who do not have work contact. Table 6–9 shows the
work contact patterns of engineers with other engineers in their field and in allied fields cross classified
with social contact patterns with the same groups.
The data clearly indicate that frequency of contact
at work is highly associated with frequency of social
contact. Also, engineers are more likely to have social
contacts with engineers in their own fields as compared to allied fields, but these differences are not
pronounced.

In general, the data indicate a moderate degree of
social contact among engineers, which may serve to
inhibit the development of strong colleague ties. This
would be quite consistent with the findings on colleague orientations reported in Chapter 4. The absence

TABLE 6-9 *Engineers Contact with Colleagues at Work and Social Contact Outside of Work*

Extent of Social Contact Outside of Work	Same Engineering Field			Allied Engineering Fields		
	Daily-Weekly	Monthly to Once a Year	Did Not Contact	Daily-Weekly	Monthly to Once a Year	Did Not Contact
Engineers in Same Field						
Daily-weekly	42%	9%	3%	45%	32%	28%
Monthly to once a year	54	81	28	51	63	53
Did not contact	4	10	69	4	5	20
Number of Engineers	1188	1681	157	903	1840	282
Engineers in Allied Fields						
Daily-weekly	31%	17%	12%	42%	13%	8%
Monthly to once a year	60	69	46	54	74	47
Did not contact	9	13	44	4	13	44
Number of Engineers	1188	1681	157	903	1840	282

of a high degree of community, however, does not
mean that the occupational group exhibits a considerable degree of "openness" in terms of social
contact with nonengineers. This could mean that a
large proportion of engineers operate pretty much on
a limited social contact diet (which would be consistent with their low people-orientation), or it might
mean that they have social contact with people who
have nothing to do with the organization in which
they are employed.

A tentative conclusion that might be drawn is that
the limited degree of occupational community has
negative consequences for the profession in terms of
colleague ties and the limited contact with nonengineers (both professional and nonprofessional).
Similarly, specialized reading behavior has negative
consequences for technical tasks dealing with planned
social change.

NOTES

1. Talcott Parsons, "The Kinship System of the Contemporary United States," *American Anthropologist,*
   45 (January-March 1943), 23–38.
2. William Lloyd Warner and James C. Abegglen, *Big
   Business Leaders in America* (New York: Atheneum,
   1963), Chaps. 6 and 7.
3. Carolyn Cummings Perrucci, "Social Origins, Mobility
   Patterns and Fertility," paper presented at the American Sociological Association meetings, San Francisco,
   August 1967.
4. Martin Gold and Carol Slater, "Office, Factory, Store
   and Family: A Study of Integration Setting," *Amer-*

ican Sociological Review, 23 (February 1958), 682–689.

5. Eugene Litwak, "Occupational Mobility and Extended Family Cohesion," *American Sociological Review,* 25 (February 1960), 9–21; Eugene Litwak, "Geographic Mobility and Extended Family Cohesion," *American Sociological Review,* 25 (June 1960), 385–394.

6. Warner and Abegglen, *op. cit.,* pp. 139–140.

7. William Lloyd Warner and James C. Abegglen, "The Personality of a Successful Man," in William Lloyd Warner and Norman Martin (eds.), *Industrial Man* (New York: Harper & Row), p. 38.

8. For a fuller discussion and analysis of the four types of orientations, see Vincent J. Salvo, "Normative Congruence and Professionalism of Engineers in Industry and Government" (unpublished manuscript, Purdue University, 1967).

9. Peter Blau, "Social Mobility and Interpersonal Relations," *American Sociological Review,* 21 (June 1956), 290–295.

10. Robert P. Stuckert, "Occupational Mobility and Family Relationships," *Social Forces,* 41 (March 1963), 301–307.

11. William H. Whyte, Jr., *The Organization Man* (New York: Simon and Schuster, 1956), Chaps. 21 and 22.

12. *Ibid.,* p. 295.

13. Saundra Kraye, "Student Typologies and Post-College Experiences: A Study of the Persistence of Orientations Among Engineers" (unpublished M.S. thesis, Purdue University, 1966).

14. Roland J. Pellegrin and Charles H. Coates, "Absentee-Owned Corporations and Community Power Structure," *American Journal of Sociology,* 61 (March 1956), 413–419.

15. Robert O. Schulze, "The Role of Economic Dominants in Community Power Structure," *American Sociological Review,* 23 (February 1958), 3–9.

16. *Ibid.,* p. 5.

17. It is interesting to note that very similar issues are raised with respect to technical experts in the Soviet Union who are continually faced with the cross pressures of politization and depolitization. See Roman

Kolkowicz, *The Soviet Army and the Communist Party: Institutions in Conflict* (Santa Monica, Calif.: Rand Corporation, August 1966).

18. Richard Wunderlich, "Freshmen Engineers: A Study of Occupational Commitment" (unpublished M.S. thesis, Purdue University, 1966).

19. Harold L. Wilensky, "Mass Society and Mass Culture," *American Sociological Review*, 29 (April 1964), 173–197. For comparable British data see J. E. Gerstl and S. P. Hutton, *Engineers: The Anatomy of a Profession* (London: Tavistock Publications, 1966), Chap. 9.

20. Carolyn Cummings Perrucci and William K. LeBold, *The Engineer and Scientist: Student, Professional and Citizen,* Purdue University Engineering Experiment Station Bulletin (Lafayette, Ind.: Purdue University, 1967).

21. For a comparison of occupations on this dimension, see Joel E. Gerstl, "Determinant of Occupational Community in High Status Occupations," *The Sociological Quarterly*, 2 (January 1961), 37–48.

7

PRESENT
AND
FUTURE

The crucial context of our analysis
of engineers and the engineering profession has been the broad trend of
increasing specialization in the occupational structure. The spiral of specialization casts professions in general,
and the new technological professions
in particular, as prime agents—and
subjects—of social change. Yet, the
understanding of the transformations
involved in so fundamental a phenomenon as the division of labor is
incommensurate with the consequences. Given the fundamental role
of professions as mechanisms of social
integration, the development of theoretical frames of reference is essential. The fusion of functional and
process models of professional analy-

sis in this volume aims to further this development.

Engineers do not merely represent a burgeoning professional category or the apotheosis of the technological-organizational society; they are also the actors playing out and creating new and distinctive sociological relationships. However prosaic the social image involved ("Slide rules will be raised in salute to the American engineer in honor of National Engineers' Week"), the sociology of engineering cannot be ignored merely for want of glamour. Neither should it be subsumed under the sociology of science, for to do so would be to lose sight of alternative issues.

At innumerable points in our analysis we confronted the theme embodied in our title: Although engineering *is* a profession, it lacks the one characteristic traditionally deemed the essence of professionalism—a community of shared values. Neither the functional models nor the process models of the professions serve to explicate this state of affairs in a satisfactory manner. Accordingly, our inquiry required a reformulation which turned out to be a salutory procedure in terms of the confrontation of theory by findings. We have attempted to synthesize the functional and process (or conflict) perspectives, since both points of view are relevant to a complete understanding of the continuing exigencies confronting professions. Not only does the dual model serve to order apparent inconsistencies in the engineering profession, but we suggest that it is a more viable vehicle generally. While functional and process models have each generated different types of research, the assumption of incompatibility has accrued without having been tested.

In considering the functional characteristics of professions we have noted the importance of on-going processes. Thus, the composition of any profession's optimal knowledge base involves a varying input of mystery, science, and aesthetics, not to mention the changing content within each of these categories over time. Similarly, in discussing the knowledge base and the related traits of autonomy, obligation, and commitment, it was emphasized that these are variables rather than present or absent conditions. They not only define professional behavior, but need to be seen as contingent upon particular exigencies of educational experience, work setting, and career patterns.

The professional touchstone, both in terms of functions and processes, serves as the basis of our depiction of engineering recruitment, education, socialization, professionalism, career patterns, and ties to family and community.

Individuals drawn to engineering careers tend to be upwardly mobile, advancing beyond their fathers' occupational level. A large proportion come from "small town" America and form a highly talented group. These characteristics, especially in combination with distinctive occupational values—low interest in people, great concern with making money, and an emphasis upon activism—describe the raw materials of engineering personnel (Chapter 2). These characteristics and values would seem to suggest an extreme vocational orientation. Yet, it appears that engineering students are not appreciably different in their orientation from the majority of American college students in most fields. Further changes that require careful attention involve the increasing interest in graduate work and research on the part of engineering undergraduates.

In contrast with the functional approach of most accounts of the socialization of preprofessionals, our

analysis of the education and socialization of engineers
(Chapter 3) reveals this stage to be characterized by
the genesis and propagation of diversity and segmentation. The factors accounting for this situation
include the abrupt changes in engineering education
in this century, the most recent involving the switch
from a practical art viewpoint to a science stressing
research and development. Thus, engineers now exist
with a variety of educational backgrounds, formal
degrees, work activities, and occupational orientations.
Further segmentation results from differing patterns
of contemporary educational programs and varying
needs of employers for engineers of particular abilities,
interests, and qualifications. In addition, the problem
of exclusive jurisdiction is compounded by the fact
that many persons holding degrees in other areas work
as engineers, and vice versa. In the midst of such
diversity and segmentation, a consistent theme is the
demanding nature of the engineering curriculum—or
more broadly, the culture of engineering schools—
which restricts the academic and social experience of
the engineering student. Although an increasing sense
of social responsibility appears to be functionally related to the engineer's role, there seems to be little
evidence that socialization is conducive to the development of sensitivity to human values.

The segmentation bred in diverse educational con-
texts is further revealed in alternative professional
values and activities (Chapter 4). The major contrast, however, is contingent upon advanced degree
work, and especially upon attainment of the Ph.D.
Apart from the importance attached to autonomy, doctorate engineers consistently adhere to professional
values more strongly than do others. Value differentiation is also related to the amount of technical re-

sponsibility involved in an engineer's position. Yet, increased administrative responsibility, unlike technical responsibility, does not reflect itself in stronger professional values. The pattern of professional activities is consistent with that of values: education and technical responsibility explain the contrasting behavior. Interestingly, many engineers in high administrative positions attend meetings without attributing much importance to colleague contact as a professional value. Beyond the differences in professional values, activities, and orientations, there is a relative absence of major conflict between organizational and professional norms concerning autonomy.

Careers in engineering once again reenforce the basic trends of segmentation (Chapter 5). Engineers experience considerable mobility between organizations. However, there appears to be remarkable stability within such functional work categories as research, development, design, operations, and management. Major variations exist concerning the degree of technical responsibility, the amount and type of supervisory responsibility, and the balance between technical and administrative aspects of work performed. The crucial contrasts, of course, are the alternative career paths of the B.S. and the Ph.D. engineer, and the subtle differences on issues such as the definition of success.

Finally, in turning to the engineer in his non-occupational roles (Chapter 6), segmental patterns appear to be less important, but still cannot be ignored. For example, it is suggested that family-career conflicts be examined in the context of career stages and their variable demands. Similarly, although the engineer is generally apolitical, civic and political involvement tends to be a function of holding higher supervisory and technical responsibility. It is significant that intellectual taste, as indicated by reading preferences, is unrelated to such factors as extent of formal education. Rather, the generalization that *the* engineer has the breadth of the middle mass appears valid, and allows little optimism concerning his capacity to fulfill social responsibilities. Colleague ties and a sense of occupational community are not dominant characteristics of any segment of the engineers. In this sense of the term, as well as in our broader usage, engineers are without community.

Emerging Patterns of Professionalism

One of the major problems discussed in this book has dealt with the great diversity in engineering that tends to limit the utility of viewing professions as homogeneous in purpose, preparation, and practice. Clearly, some professions are more homogeneous than others, reflecting greater selectivity in recruitment, more intense professional socialization, and more predictable and rewarding career development. The role of professions in modern society exhibits several trends toward strengthening the professional community and further challenging its viability as an occupational institution.

The first trend is the growing involvement of professionals in organizational careers. With the exception of medicine and law, practitioners in established and emerging professions carry out their activities in large scale settings controlled by operational procedures that limit their sphere of freedom. Yet, even law and medicine are not entirely free of this trend, for there is an apparent movement toward group practice rather than private practice. Clearly, for engineers the overwhelming pattern is not only employment in organizational settings, but employment in organizations containing thousands of employees.

Employment in organizational settings will challenge the traditional professional values of autonomy in the conduct of one's work, and of colleague control over the sanctions for rewarding or punishing individual practitioners. Moreover, organizational employment will result in greater opportunities for managerial and supervisory careers that take the practitioner out of direct professional activity. The consequence of this will be less attachment to the professional career since it is no longer terminal in nature, and no longer contains the greatest rewards in power and income (and perhaps even prestige). If we see the engineer as the forerunner of the new organizational professional, it is clear that the loss of colleague-based rewards will result in greater susceptibility to the alternative organizational rewards attached to managerial positions.

A second emerging trend is the tendency of professionals' clients, public, or employers to resist the process of professionalization in the sense of disputing who is to control the professional's performance, and questioning either the quality of professional knowledge or the quantity of available practitioners. We see the challenge to the quantity and quality of professional performance in several areas. Teachers are so concerned with preparing college-bound students in science and mathematics that they have lost sight of the needs of the "average" students, especially those in inner city schools; nurses have become so preoccupied with the esoteric knowledge of medicine that they no longer understand patient needs for the nurse with a bedside manner who dispenses warmth, understanding, and treatment of emotional needs; engineers are now thoroughly prepared in science, mathematics, and the engineering sciences with the result that they are unlikely to be satisfied with the mundane technical tasks that are essential to the work of a large majority of engineers.

The response to any perceived inadequacy in professional performance is often the creation of new nonprofessional roles designed to meet needs that the full professional either can not or will not meet. Thus, a growing cry in many schools in the inner city has been for the creation of new resident-teacher roles to bring adults who live in the inner city into the schools to fill supportive educational roles. What the new nonprofessional lacks in formal knowledge will be more than compensated for by closer social and emotional ties to students and increased sensitivity to student needs. A similar pattern is seen in nursing where there is a growing interest in intermediate nursing roles, such as nurse's aides. Thus, the professionalized nurse spends less and less time with patients, and the nurse's aide spends more time with housekeeping activities on the ward and with tending the basic physical needs of patients. The new nonprofessional would be more closely concerned with the bedside role of dealing with patients as people rather than as units in an organization or as interesting medical entities.

In engineering we find the emergence of the nonprofessional roles of engineering technician and technologist. The demand for the new engineering roles again stems from the clients' or employers' belief that the performance of engineers is inadequate. The immediate effect of these new programs will be to recruit a larger proportion of the thousands of students now entering most engineering programs by encouraging them to pursue their interests in traditional engineering work rather than in the engineering-science programs. Under such conditions, current undergraduate engineering programs will move more rapidly in the direction of an undergraduate pre-engineering degree with advanced degree education required for full professional status. The trend will be toward greater specialization of educational functions and a more restricted distribution of the title of professional engineer.

This will lead to greater homogeneity of interests and aspirations of persons pursuing advanced degrees in engineering for the attainment of full professional status. Preprofessional undergraduate curricula would probably be unified, eliminating much of the present diversity within the profession. However, at the same time that the profession is strengthened in terms of requiring advanced degrees for professional status and minimizing the diversity of backgrounds, education, and work function engineers, there will also be a challenge that stems from the loss of exclusive rights to perform engineering functions. It may well be that the graduates of engineering technician and technology programs may more than satisfy the needs of industry, leaving the professional engineer with the doctorate degree as a luxury that is needed or can be afforded by only a limited number of users.

All this is, of course, speculation, but it does seem to follow what may be an emerging pattern of professionalization and deprofessionalization. In dealing with engineering in this book, emphasis was put upon the sources of diversity and segmentation that served as barriers to the emergence of a unified, internally homogeneous profession. As the profession has developed, there have been two different trends emerging: one toward increasing the quality and quantity of engineering education that emphasizes graduate degrees, science, and mathematics; the other toward a reaffirmation of the practical-applied emphasis in engineering with a minimum of education in terms of length, depth, and diversity. The first trend places the control over engineering in the hands of practitioners. It is less sensitive to the needs of clients or users. Under such conditions the values of autonomy, colleague control, and collective identification with a career are likely to emerge. The other trend gives a greater role to the client or user of engineering talent to determine the character of the expertise that the engineer should have. Under such conditions engineers should think of themselves more as skilled employees than as professionals.

The extent to which special preprofessional or nonprofessional roles emerge in response to perceived inadequacies by clients and users depends very much upon the extent of institutionalized power that the profession has in determining who may or may not practice. Medicine is an example of a profession with well-institutionalized power, and it would seem unlikely that clients could force a change in medical professional roles. What is more likely to occur is a growing negative public attitude toward the profession without the prospect of increasing public control over performance. In more vulnerable professions like the clergy, nursing, teaching, and engineering, we would expect greater elaboration of nonprofessional roles designed to meet the client needs that are neglected in the process of professionalization.

As engineering moves toward a more homogeneous, internally strong profession composed of practitioners with advanced degrees and with strong professional commitments, we would expect to find a strong counter trend of deprofessionalizing engineering work. Such counter trends will produce debate and conflict over who has the right to be called an engineer and to do engineering work. They may also reintroduce an interest in unionism as a unifying force in the new nonprofessional engineering roles.

While it seems clear that engineers will not emerge as the rulers of the technocracy envisioned by Veblen, it does seem that their emergent involvement as planners, designers, and guardians of technical-social systems has far greater significance for the future of American society.

Index

187